'You are jeal[...]
Slade mocke[...]

'Of course not[...]
head. 'But I re[...]
yourself and another for me.'

'Then I must disabuse you of any such notion.
For the duration of this trip, you're my wife
and I shall act accordingly.'

A tremor swept through Eden. 'H-How do you
mean?'

'I mean that the only woman I shall favour with
my kisses will be you.'

Dear Reader

As the dark winter nights unfold, what better to turn to than a heart-warming Mills & Boon! As usual, we bring you a selection of books which take you all over the world, with heroines you like and heroes you would love to be with! So take a flight of fancy away from everyday life to the wonderful world of Mills & Boon—you'll be glad you did.

The Editor

Valerie Parv was a successful journalist and non-fiction writer until she began writing for Mills & Boon in 1982. Born in Shropshire, England, she grew up in Australia and now lives with her cartoonist husband and their cat— the office manager—in Sydney, New South Wales. She is a keen futurist, a *Star Trek* enthusiast, and her interests include travelling, restoring dolls' houses and entertaining friends. Writing romance novels affirms her belief in love and happy endings.

Recent titles by the same author:

LOVERS' MOON

FLIGHT OF FANTASY

BY
VALERIE PARV

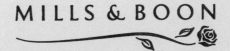

MILLS & BOON

MILLS & BOON LIMITED
ETON HOUSE, 18-24 PARADISE ROAD
RICHMOND, SURREY TW9 1SR

First published in Great Britain 1993 by Mills & Boon Limited

© Valerie Parv 1993

Australian copyright 1993 Philippine copyright 1993 This edition 1993

ISBN 0 263 78301 4

Set in Times Roman 11 on 12 pt. 01-9312-48526 C

Made and printed in Great Britain

CHAPTER ONE

EDEN LYLE cupped a hand over her free ear, straining to hear the telephone over the hubbub in the airport departure lounge. Suddenly her unfocused gaze was caught and held by an arresting figure striding purposefully through the throng.

'It can't be,' she murmured.

'Can't be who?' came the ungrammatical response down the line.

Eden dragged her attention back to her call. 'I thought I saw my boss a moment ago.'

Fiona's chuckle crackled between them. 'What would Slade Benedict be doing at Hobart Airport? I thought he was back at your office breaking in his new production assistant.'

'You mean his new *male* assistant,' Eden said with heavy emphasis. Her shoulder-length ash-brown hair fell forward, hiding the hurt which sprang into her amethyst eyes. It was hard to accept that Slade had brought in a man from outside his corporate communications company to fill the job she had worked towards for months.

'Hey, I thought this trip was supposed to cheer you up. Forget chauvinistic Mr Benedict.'

Eden's sigh travelled down the phone. 'You're right as usual.' Both of them knew how much Eden needed this break. Nothing had gone right lately, and now the pattern seemed set to continue. Only one flight was leaving Hobart this morning. Was Slade planning to be on it? 'What is he *doing* here?' she voiced her misgivings.

'He might be meeting someone off the Melbourne flight,' Fiona reasoned, trying to defuse the tension in Eden's voice.

Although she murmured agreement, Eden's eyes remained fixed on the man. It probably wasn't Slade at all. The fact that he stood a head taller than the people around him and his wide shoulders strained the impeccable lines of a designer business suit didn't mean it was her boss. Lots of men were tall and broad.

But they didn't all move with the lithe grace of a predator stalking its terrain, she thought. The easy confidence of the man's movements was disturbingly familiar, as was his gesture when he lifted a long-fingered hand to brush a strand of charcoal hair back behind one ear.

'Eden, are you still there?'

At Fiona's sharp tone, she made an effort to concentrate on the call which she had initiated, after all. 'Yes, I'm still here. I wanted to be sure that Mum has settled down all right. Just lately, I've had the feeling that something's bothering her, but she can't or won't tell me what it is.'

Fiona sighed. 'Whatever it is, she'll tell you when she's ready. Now stop worrying. Shepherd House is the best place she could possibly be. I know, I worked there myself for a time and they have tons of expertise in genetic problems like your mother's. Believe me, they'll take excellent care of Peggy.'

'I don't want her to be unhappy. I know we haven't always been as close as I'd like but...'

'But she'd be even less happy if you *don't* take this holiday,' Fiona insisted. 'Do you think she doesn't know what a burden she's become to you? Maybe that's what she's been trying to tell you.'

'She isn't a burden,' Eden denied hotly. 'Although she's a little difficult at times, she's still my mother and I want the best for her.'

'As I'm sure she appreciates. But if the roles were reversed wouldn't you want to give your daughter a break if you could?'

'I suppose so.' Eden hadn't considered it from her mother's point of view. Given Peggy's sometimes over-possessive behaviour, it had come as a surprise when she insisted that a small legacy be used to pay for a spell in a nursing home while Eden took a much needed holiday. Fiona had reduced her fees to the bare minimum, but paying her to look after Peggy during the day left nothing over for holidays, far less pay for full-time care while Eden went away.

'You've been so good to us, Fiona,' she said, her voice catching.

'Get away with you.' Fiona's Scottish brogue coloured her voice, betraying her emotions. 'Your mother was a pleasure to look after.'

'We'll miss you,' Eden added. 'Don't forget to send us a postcard from Scotland.'

'I'll miss you, too.' The nurse was taking a holiday of her own to visit relatives in her birthplace. 'Send me a card yourself, if you aren't too involved with some gorgeous Queensland hunk.'

'Fat chance,' Eden laughed, but felt a pang as she hung up the phone. She had tried romance only once, with a man she'd met through work. Joshua

Robinson had seemed like the ideal man for her, tender yet strong, and lots of fun to be with.

Their dates had been limited to the times she could afford to pay Fiona for after-hours care for her mother. Joshua didn't seem to mind, telling her how much he admired what she was doing for Peggy. 'There aren't many girls like you, Eden,' he had told her admiringly.

He was right in a sense. Not many girls had her problems to cope with. When Joshua found out what they were, the relationship had come to a sudden end.

Anguish darkened her eyes. Telling herself she was better off without him didn't help. The memories of the good times were too powerful. She'd been so sure of him.

Just goes to show how little I know about love, she told herself, trying for flippancy and failing miserably. Darn it, Joshua's rejection still hurt. He had no right to offer her a shining view of a shared future then make it conditional on her being perfect. Even assuring Joshua that her mother's illness always skipped a generation hadn't helped.

He didn't love her enough to accept her as she was. There it was in a nutshell. Maybe all men were like Joshua and her father, who had left the family while Eden was still a teenager, before her mother's illness became apparent. He had missed the worst of Peggy's gradual decline, which had only recently led to her requiring full-time nursing. If he couldn't cope with Peggy's possessive nature before she became ill he wouldn't have fared much better afterwards, Eden acknowledged.

Men! If they all required perfection from their women, she was probably better off without them. And that definitely included Slade Benedict, she resolved.

Nevertheless, she found herself scanning the crowd for a broad-shouldered man, telling herself it was only to prove that he was a total stranger. To her mild chagrin, there was no sign of him.

There was another surprise in store for her at the check-in counter when she handed over her suitcase and received her boarding pass. 'There must be some mistake,' she said to the attendant. 'According to this, I've been allocated a seat in first class.'

The man glanced at the pass and back to his computer screen, punching keys with deft fingers. 'No mistake, Miss Lyle. Everything's in order. Enjoy your flight.'

'But...'

Behind her, the queue was lengthening and people stirred restively. A suitcase was dumped on to the check-point beside her, giving her little option but to move away from the counter, clutching the pass.

She should be pleased to have been moved up into first class. The fare was more than double what she'd paid for her excursion ticket and she'd been charged no more. All the same, uneasiness etched a frown into the alabaster skin of her forehead, drawing curious glances from the people who eddied around her.

There was also admiration in the looks. Her romantic, softly curving figure was set off to perfection in a new turquoise-spotted dress with matching white crop-topped jacket, a pert spotted hanky spilling from the breast pocket.

She had been reluctant to spend the money for the outfit but now felt relieved. At least she wouldn't look out of place among the first-class passengers. That was it! The economy section must have been overbooked, forcing the airline to up-grade some of the passengers. It was probably this very outfit which had prompted them to choose her.

Relieved that she had solved the puzzle, she spun around, intending to return to the counter and thank the obliging clerk, only to cannon into a broad, masculine body.

'I'm so sorry,' she gasped as steely fingers clamped around her upper arms to steady her. 'I wasn't looking where I was going.'

'As it happens, you're just the woman I'm looking for.'

A gasp tore from her throat as she recognised the voice and looked up into a pair of all too familiar grey-green eyes. She was so close that she could see the tracery of yellow lines which went from the pupils to the outer edges of his irises like the spokes of a wheel. The effect was mesmerising.

The thought that she was the woman he was looking for left her momentarily speechless, until she realised he meant it in a business sense. Fool, she chided herself. Why else would a man like him want her? 'Slade...I mean, Mr Benedict...' she muttered when she finally summoned her voice.

'Slade will do in the circumstances,' he demurred.

In what circumstances? Had she left something vital undone at the office?

He still held her in a steadying grip, his long fingers firm around her arms. The heat travelled through her skin as if it had been touched by a branding iron. Without putting up an unseemly struggle she couldn't twist free, so she willed herself to calmness. 'I'm leaving in half an hour for the Sunshine Coast.'

'I know.'

'You do?' As the words tumbled out she cursed her own stupidity. Of course he knew. He had approved her request for leave. She was annoyed by her own responses. He might be all-powerful over his employees but he had no right to detain her now, when her time was her own.

'You said you were looking for me?' she prompted, her tone cool to indicate that she didn't welcome his intrusion.

He glanced at the boarding pass she still clutched in nerveless fingers. As if she hadn't spoken, he nodded tautly. 'You've checked in already? Good. Let's go somewhere we can talk.'

Releasing her at last, he turned away as if fully expecting her to follow him. Her annoyance grew and she stood her ground. 'Did I leave something unfinished at the office?'

The question caught him by surprise. 'Not that I know of.' But at least he stood still, regarding her with ill-concealed impatience.

'Then why do we need to talk? If it's about the promotion, I've already apologised for what I said.'

He looked puzzled, then annoyed. But he couldn't have forgotten her foolish outburst after she learned that he had appointed a man from outside the company to fill the production vacancy.

She had been counting on the promotion to provide a much needed salary increase to give her mother a few extra luxuries. To have the job go to a man who didn't even work for Benedict Communications had come as a bitter blow. She had said as much to her co-worker when the decision was announced.

'Our male chauvinist boss strikes again,' Denise, the researcher who worked with Eden, had responded as they helped themselves to coffee from the dispenser.

Spooning sugar into her cup, Eden had regarded Denise with disbelief. 'You don't think he overlooked me because I'm female?'

Denise shrugged. 'What other reason can there be? You have all the necessary qualifications. You've filled in as an assistant producer when someone's ill or on holiday, and you have the seniority. As far as I can tell, your only flaw is your sex.'

'But that sort of discrimination is illegal.'

'Tell that to our fearless leader. You'll notice there's a dearth of female talent in the top echelons of his empire.'

Eden sipped her coffee thoughtfully. 'I hadn't noticed, but you're right.'

'Therefore, Slade Benedict is allergic to putting women into top jobs.'

'He certainly isn't allergic to women,' Eden pointed out. In the social columns, Slade was regularly paired with some famous beauty or other.

'Too true, but in the bedroom, not the boardroom.'

Denise's irreverence was already making Eden feel better. 'Slade Benedict prefers his women in the bedroom rather than the boardroom.' She savoured the phrase. Since she couldn't change her sex, it was less hurtful than being denied promotion because she wasn't good enough.

'It would be enlightening to know on what grounds you base your assessment,' came a chilly voice close behind her.

Denise's appalled expression told Eden not only that Slade was there, but that he had heard every word.

'I—er—none, really,' she dissembled.

She half turned to find him leaning against the wall with apparent indolence, his arms crossed over his broad chest. The seeming casualness of the pose was belied by the challenging fire which flashed in his grey eyes.

He was waiting for her to back her accusation of his sexism with facts, but she had none. Backing down wouldn't help either, instinct told her. She had got herself into this so there was nothing for it but to brazen it out.

'We were discussing the lack of females in the top ranks of the firm,' she said, unconsciously straightening to her full five feet seven inches. It still left her a good four inches short of meeting him eyeball to eyeball.

Grudging respect flitted across his face before his gaze hardened. 'Whom I appoint to my management team is hardly your concern, Miss Lyle. I presume this has something to do with your missing out on the production appointment?'

She felt the ground giving way beneath her but had come too far to retreat now. 'Yes, it does. My qualifications are the equal of those of the man you appointed to the job.'

'So you've decided that I rejected you because you're a woman.' His blatantly appraising gaze left her in no doubt that he was well aware of the fact, and she felt heat rising into her face. The assessment was so flagrantly sexual that her anger flared. How dared he treat her so disrespectfully?

She opened her mouth to protest but the wind was taken out of her sails when he cut across her. 'I see you object to being judged on the basis of your sex. Yet that's precisely what you were doing to me a moment ago, was it not?'

It was true, she *had* been judging him, not on the facts but on pure hearsay. 'You're right and I apologise,' she said unreservedly.

'Accepted,' he said evenly. 'I approved your application for leave this morning, you'll be glad to hear.'

'I hope it isn't an inconvenient time for me to go,' she said, seizing on the change of subject. 'I'm taking a package holiday to the Sunshine Coast and the choice of departure dates is limited.'

'Good, good,' he dismissed the trivial details impatiently, then fixed her with a penetrating look. 'Use the time to think things through and you'll realise I made the right decision about the promotion. You're a capable, enthusiastic researcher but it takes a lot more to make an assistant producer. Maturity and judgement for a start. Maybe in a year or two you'll have attained them.'

He strode off towards the executive offices, leaving Denise staring open-mouthed after him. She hadn't dared to speak after he joined them, and now gave Eden a shocked look. 'I'm sorry it was my smart remark which got you into trouble.'

'It isn't your fault. I didn't have to repeat it,' she said with great fairness. She was still smarting from the frankly sexual way he had appraised her. Or was it her own instinctive reaction which shocked her?

Even while raging at his behaviour, some part of her had responded to it with chemical vibrancy. It was as if he had flipped a switch to 'on' deep inside her, setting hundreds of nerve-endings pulsating in sympathetic resonance.

He had turned her on. The evocative phrase was the only one which fitted her reaction, yet she refused to believe she could feel anything but fury towards him. He hadn't denied promoting men rather than women to the top jobs in his company. If anything, his behaviour had confirmed his view of women as sex objects.

She had gone home that night and taken out her impotent rage on the housework, polishing floors with the same savage intensity that she would have liked to apply to removing the smug expression from his handsome features.

If he knew how he had affected her, he had given no sign of it, accepting her apology at face value and treating her much the same as always. Which was to say with businesslike coolness, until she left to go on holiday. And now he wanted to go somewhere to talk? 'I can't,' she denied. 'My plane...'

'Leaves in half an hour,' he reiterated. 'You already pointed it out. Not that you needed to. It's my flight, too.'

'You're going to the Sunshine Coast too?'

The amusement in his gaze taunted her. 'Do you have any objections?'

'Of course not.' But she did and she had a feeling he knew it. Before she could ask any more questions he took her arm in a grip which looked courteous but felt like steel, as he steered her towards the departure lounge.

In the quiet, luxurious surroundings of the first-class lounge, he led her to a secluded group of armchairs which looked like a corner of an expensively furnished private home. 'Wait here. I'll get you a drink.'

She gathered her wits enough to say, 'Something soft, please.' Slade Benedict's sudden appearance was heady enough without compounding the effects with alcohol. She was furious about his take-charge behaviour but also consumed with curiosity. What on earth could he want to talk about?

It couldn't be about her childish outburst over the promotion. He had accepted her apology and, despite his arrogance, he wasn't the type of man to carry a grudge.

Even so, she wished she could take the outburst back. It would have been better to approach him with her concerns in a calm, rational manner. No wonder he thought she lacked maturity.

There was another possibility and she bit her lip, thinking of it. When she'd joined his company, there had been a misunderstanding about her age which she hadn't corrected. As a result, she had

started at a higher level and salary than her qualifications deserved.

Determined not to cheat anyone, she had
crammed every bit of experience she could into her
workday, taking courses and skipping breaks until
she was sure the company was getting more than
its money's worth from her. Could Slade have
found out somehow? Would he think her hard work
was enough to balance out that one lapse when she
was hired?

His stony expression as he approached with their
drinks did nothing for her peace of mind. Then
common sense came to her aid. If he *had* found
out, he would have fired her, not allowed her to go
on leave.

She forced herself to relax but it was a challenge
as he dropped into a chair at right angles to her
own. Stretching his long legs out, he hooked one
foot over the other. Her own legs started to ache
from keeping them tucked primly beneath her but
the discomfort was preferable to the risk of tangling
her legs with his.

Her tension grew and she looked at her watch.
'My flight will be boarding soon. Hadn't you better
tell me what this is all about?'

'Our flight,' he corrected. 'Don't worry, they'll
page us in here after the others are aboard.'

'You arranged for me to be in first class, didn't
you?' she said on a sudden suspicion.

'I wondered when the penny would drop.'

'It's more than a penny, it's several hundred
dollars,' she gasped, finding her feet at last. 'I
thought the airline was responsible. Now I know it

was your doing, I can't possibly agree. I could never afford to pay you back.'

'I don't expect you to,' he said mildly.

'But you do expect something?'

It was hardly a question. Men like Slade Benedict always balanced the scales somehow.

She was totally unprepared for his answer. 'I do want something in return. I want you to be my wife.'

She sat down again before her legs collapsed under her, and took a swallow of the drink he'd provided. 'You want what?'

'Relax. This isn't a new form of seduction. I want you to act the part for the next few days.'

This was crazy! He might be her boss but he had no right to make such an outrageous demand. 'I'm sorry, but I'm no actress,' she denied.

His eyes narrowed, his gaze chilling. 'Oh, no? My perusal of your personnel file suggests quite the opposite.'

So he did know that she was masquerading as older than her real age. 'I needed the job,' she said by way of vindication. 'I didn't mean any harm. And you must agree that I've done a good job.'

'Which is the only reason you are still employed in my organisation,' he assented. 'Your work is outstanding, not that I would have accepted less.'

'But it was the reason why I didn't get the promotion,' she conceded.

'Yes, it was. I feel you need a few more years' experience in your present position, until you catch up with the age you purport to be.'

He steepled his fingers and looked thoughtful. 'How old are you, incidentally?'

'Twenty-five,' she said in a barely audible tone. At work she was supposed to be nearing her thirtieth birthday. Surely, knowing the truth, he would drop his alarming request for her to act as his wife? The newspapers had reported his own thirtieth birthday over a year ago, so he must see how incompatible they were, on age alone.

'Twenty-five,' he mused. 'It's a little young but you've been passing as older successfully so it will have to do.'

Distantly, she heard the first call for their flight, but was too preoccupied to pay it much attention. How dared he assume she would fall in with his plans simply because he willed it?

'All the same, I can't act as your wife,' she declared. What right did he have to ask such a thing? 'I don't even know you, at least, not in that way.'

His grim look lightened slightly. 'You don't have to know me—in that way,' he said, deliberately misinterpreting her words. 'There are no sexual favours involved so don't look so affronted. I'm not looking for a wife in the literal sense.'

Did she imagine it or did he shudder slightly at the prospect of being tied down with a wife? No wonder he had to proposition her at an airport to fill the role, if he found the idea of marriage so repulsive.

'Nevertheless, I take your point that we need to appear more familiar with one another than we do now,' he went on. 'An evening together should be sufficient. It can be easily arranged, as we're staying in the same hotel.'

'Which you no doubt arranged at the same time as you had my airline ticket upgraded,' she assumed furiously. Boss or not, he was the most high-handed man she had ever met. If ever she went shopping for a husband, she would wish for someone a little more human than Slade seemed to be.

'I'm sorry but I can't help you,' she said flatly, her voice vibrant with anger. 'I don't know why you're asking me but no reason could possibly justify it.'

'Not even the lives of hundreds of Aboriginal babies?' he said blandly.

About to thank him for the drink and walk away, she froze. 'What did you say?'

'I said that your agreement to what is really a simple task could save hundreds of young lives.'

'I don't understand.'

He leaned closer, enfolding her in the potent male aura of his aftershave lotion so that she felt slightly light-headed. 'The resort you're booked into is also the venue for a business convention which I'm attending, along with some friends from my university days.'

'If this is some kind of practical joke...'

'It's no joke,' he said grimly. 'At university, a group of us invested some money with the agreement that the last one to remain single would claim what has become a sizeable amount of money.'

She took a steadying sip of her drink. 'And you don't want the money?'

She knew without being told that Slade's business had made him one of Tasmania's richest men. 'As you're aware, I hardly need it,' he confirmed. 'But the other candidate does. Bob Hamilton, the only other bachelor, is a doctor who has devoted his life to setting up clinics for Aboriginal children in the outback. The money would greatly assist him in his work.'

More confused than ever, she shook her head. 'Then why don't you just give it to him?'

'Bob's damned pride would prevent him accepting unless he thinks he's won it fairly.'

'So when you found out I'd be there at the same time you decided to turn up with a wife to convince him that he's entitled to the money,' she summarised her understanding of the situation.

'Exactly.' He stood up. 'That's the final call for our flight. Can I take it that you'll do as I ask?'

Miserably, she shook her head. 'I wish I could, since it's in a good cause, but I'd be no good at it, honestly. I couldn't convince anyone that we're husband and wife.'

His expression became glacial. 'I hoped you'd be more helpful, Eden. That's why I kept your file on my desk instead of returning it to Personnel.'

Was he making it a choice between doing as he asked and losing her job? 'I can't believe you'd be so cruel,' she ground out. 'I've done nothing wrong.'

'Beyond accepting a job under false pretences,' he reminded her. 'After that, pretending to be my wife should be a piece of cake for you.'

A piece she might choke on, she thought. But what choice did he leave her? If she resigned, who else would employ her when he refused her a reference? 'Everything I've heard about you is true,' she said through clenched teeth. 'You're arrogant, unprincipled and manipulative.'

'But you'll do as I ask?'

'For no longer than is absolutely necessary to convince your Bob Hamilton that the money is his,' she insisted.

'Naturally,' he agreed, his mocking tone making her want to hit him. When he took her arm to escort her to the plane, it was all she could do not to tear herself free. She had better get used to it in her new role as his wife.

Slade Benedict's wife. The very thought sent surges of electric sensation pulsating through her. She told herself it was anger at the way he had virtually blackmailed her into playing the part. After all, what else could it be?

CHAPTER TWO

THE Sunshine Coast airport with its plush lounges and tropical gardens was a far cry from the sandy patch of Maroochy Beach where the first aircraft landing in the region took place in 1922.

In those days, guests stayed in boarding houses designed in traditional Queensland style with wide, airy verandas but little in the way of luxuries. Today, their plane was met by a uniformed resort driver who whisked them in air-conditioned comfort to a new, low-rise resort hotel which fronted Coolum Beach.

With the exception of a central core, the resort had no building higher than three floors. They nestled into the curve of the landscape, the colours chosen to echo the natural surroundings.

Although sharply conscious of the man at her side who was supposed to be her husband, Eden was distracted by the patterns of light and texture the design created with its clever use of roof angles, overhangs and lattices.

As their driver pointed out the resort's own large tract of coastal rainforest alongside the golf fairways, she gave a sigh of longing. If only Slade hadn't come along with his impossible demands, she would have looked forward to exploring the resort.

She jumped when he enquired solicitously, 'Ready, darling? We're here.'

They had arrived at Reception and their luggage was already being unloaded. A uniformed doorman held the limousine door for her to alight. Slade's casual use of the endearment brought the colour rising to her cheeks and she ducked her head. It was one thing to agree to act as his wife but quite another to actually carry it out.

'I something the matter, darling?' he asked, materialising at her side.

'Must you keep calling me that?'

'It's good practice,' he said, unperturbed.

'But everyone doesn't have to think we're married, only your doctor friend.'

'Who is a highly intelligent man,' Slade warned her. 'The more comfortable we become with our roles, the more convincing we'll be.'

'I suppose so,' she said on a sigh. 'I hadn't bargained on starting so soon.'

'You didn't find it difficult to keep up your act at work,' he reminded her. 'Why should it be a problem now?'

Fresh colour flamed in her cheeks, sparked by anger this time. 'All right, so I was in the wrong, but I'm doing my penance. Must you keep reminding me of it?'

'Only when you need encouraging to play the part you agreed to.'

She tossed her long hair expressively. 'Was blackmailed into, you mean. The only redeeming feature is knowing that some underprivileged children will benefit from having my holiday ruined.'

The hand she fluttered to express her frustration was captured in a firm grip. 'It needn't be ruined,' he said in a soft undertone. 'My wife is entitled to enjoy herself while she's here.'

She felt an instant lifting of her spirits which she refused to connect with the warmth of his fingers entwined with hers. 'She is? I mean . . . I am? You mean it's all right if I explore the rainforest and the wildlife sanctuary?'

Her naïve enthusiasm elicited a smile which softened the angles of his face, making him look almost attractive. 'Of course. You're free to explore while I attend the conference events. Provided you're at my side at the opening and social occasions, the rest of the time is your own. Of course, that freedom doesn't extend to holiday flirtations, you understand?'

Steel fingers crept up and down her spine, chilling her with the reminder of her unwanted obligation. 'Of course not,' she mocked. 'How would it look if Slade Benedict's *wife* was seen flirting with another man?'

His hand clamped around her wrist, drawing her irresistibly closer until his lips brushed the curve of her ear. 'I warn you not to try my patience, Eden. I want your word that you'll go through with this to the best of your ability.'

The alternative was disgrace and, quite probably, long-term unemployment. Besides, it was in a good cause, as he had just reminded her. 'You have my word,' she agreed. 'Now will you release my hand? You're hurting me.'

'Not as much as I will if you go back on your promise,' he vowed. But his fingers loosened and she retrieved her wrist, rubbing it significantly so that he would know how bruising his grip had been.

But there was worse to come, she found when they were shown to their accommodation.

'You can't expect me to share a room with you,' she seethed in an undertone, her glance moving to the porter who was delivering their luggage.

Slade's eyebrows lifted in mocking amusement. 'Not a room, a suite. Married couples usually share sleeping quarters.'

Despair throbbed through her. Despite his assurance, she was beginning to wonder how far he intended to take this charade. 'Married couples, maybe. But we're not...'

'Not in need of another thing,' he said, lifting his voice as the porter approached them. He accepted Slade's generous tip with a salute and left, closing the door behind him.

She was alone with Slade for the first time and a confusing medley of sensations assailed her. The sense of alarm, she understood. The prospect of sharing close quarters with him was enough to alarm any woman. But there was something else, too, an undercurrent of excitement which was even more shocking.

'This wasn't part of our agreement,' she denied, annoyed by the betraying tremor which vibrated in her voice. She had the uncomfortable certainty that he saw through her façade of coolness to the cauldron of emotions seething inside her.

'Scared, Eden?' he asked in a voice as soft as a caress.

'N-no.' It was true, wasn't it?

His aura enveloped her as he came up behind her, resting his hands lightly on her shoulders, the warmth of them pervading her body. 'Good. You shouldn't be scared of me, ever.'

Weakness invaded her limbs. 'Then you understand why I can't possibly agree to share your suite?'

'I understand why you don't wish to, but it's necessary.' His finger slid down her throat and came to rest on the pulse which fluttered like a caged bird. 'Most women would find the prospect stimulating.'

Her throbbing pulse betrayed how stimulating she found it, which was precisely why she dared not agree. For a heartbeat, she wondered what it would be like if she was really his wife, sharing this suite and . . . so much more.

Shocked by the power of her thoughts, she wrenched free and went to the glass door which opened on to a wide terrace, fixing her gaze on the ocean view while she fought for composure.

'All the same, I can't stay,' she said when her throat allowed words to pass again.

He spoke so close behind her that she jumped. 'You have no choice, I'm afraid. The hotel is booked out for the conference.'

Her eyebrows winged upwards. 'What about my original reservation?'

'Cancelled in favour of this one.'

A shiver propelled itself down her spine. She tried to tell herself she was affronted by his high-handedness, but the sense of rising excitement drowned it out. 'You were pretty sure I'd agree,' she said with a coolness she was far from experiencing.

He gave a crooked smile at which her heart did a kind of somersault. 'I felt confident I could persuade you.'

Her throat dried as she visualised his methods of persuasion. She had the feeling they would be devastatingly effective. Enjoyable, too, a traitorous inner voice insisted.

'I also counted on your ambition to overcome any lingering scruples you might have about the arrangements,' he added.

Surprise flared in her amethyst gaze. 'My ambition?'

'You needn't pretend with me,' he said, confusing her all the more. 'Anyone who bluffs her way into a job as you did, then works as hard as you've done to keep it, has to be ambitious. The number of courses you attend and the hours you put in speak for themselves.'

He was also well aware of her determination to gain promotion, she thought. It painted a different picture of her from the true one. Yet she couldn't defend herself without explaining that most of it was for her mother's sake, which she had no intention of doing.

The strength of her reluctance caught her by surprise. She didn't want his pity, but there was another reason, she recognised unwillingly. She liked having Slade treat her as a desirable woman and it would end as soon as he knew the truth. Didn't she have enough experience of what happened with first her father, then Joshua? She didn't want to go through such anguish ever again.

'What is it, Eden?' Slade asked, shattering her reverie as he touched a finger to her chin, tilting her face up to him.

The light touch against her throat and the intense concern she glimpsed in his eyes was almost too much. Then common sense asserted itself. 'Nothing, why?'

'For a moment, you looked incredibly sad, as if the weight of the world was on your shoulders.' His hands slid down, coming to rest on the top of her arms. 'They're much too slight for such a burden.'

Choked by feelings which threatened to overwhelm her, she spun away on to the terrace. 'I'm tougher than I look.'

She felt rather than heard his change of demeanour. His voice was cold when he said, 'I don't doubt it. Someone with your ambition would have to be.'

No, no, you're wrong about me, she wanted to deny—then immediately questioned why she should care what he thought. Wasn't it better if he accepted his own explanation of her behaviour, rather than sought the real one?

She affected a bright smile as she turned back to him. 'You're right, of course. Now which bedroom do you want me to take?'

A wry smile spilled across his features. 'I don't suppose there's any point in saying mine?'

'None at all,' she said briskly, striving to control her heartbeat, which contrarily picked up speed at the very idea. 'It wasn't part of our agreement.'

He gave an exaggerated shake of his head in mock-disappointment. 'What a pity.'

It was only as she settled into the master bedroom which he generously allocated to her, complete with its own terrace and ocean view, that she realised how restrictive this arrangement must be to *him*.

By ruling out holiday flirtations for her, a supposedly married woman, he had also ruled out casual sex for himself. If the reports of his love life were even partially true, celibacy was not his preferred state.

Her uneasy glance went to the closed door which separated them. She could hear him humming under his breath as he mixed a drink for himself, she having already declined one. She hoped he had his male hormones firmly under control because she had no intentions of taking this make-believe marriage any further. Slade Benedict was arrogant, unfeeling and iron-willed. His readiness to commandeer her holiday for his own purposes was proof enough. She would be crazy to let him use her any further, when she knew from past experience how it was bound to end.

All the same, there was something about him which haunted her. His power over her job and pay cheque couldn't explain it. This was much more intimate and disturbing, and she slammed her suitcase lid down hard, as if she could also put a lid on her thoughts. The sound reverberated through the suite, reminding Eden that she hadn't heard any sounds from the other room for a while. Slade had said he intended to check out the conference venue, as he would be giving an address next day, so he must have gone to do so.

Cautiously, she opened her bedroom door and stepped into the living-room which separated their sleeping quarters. The remains of his drink sat on a side-table, a film of moisture beading the glass. Lazily she traced a pattern in the moisture then withdrew hastily. It was only his glass, for goodness' sake. She should throw it in his face, not dream over it. What on earth was getting into her?

Her wandering gaze was arrested by several items lying behind the glass. Slade must have emptied his pockets before going out.

She ignored the jumble of keys, tickets and other paraphernalia, drawn instead to an open ticket wallet in which she glimpsed some photographs. Slade's family? The temptation to peek was irresistible.

They were indeed family snaps, she found when she drew them towards her. One was of Slade wrestling an enormous black dog, a Newfoundland, Eden noted. He looked more relaxed and happy than she had ever seen him at the office. The second photo was a studio portrait of a young girl of about nine or ten. Her face was set in such a wistful expression that Eden's heart constricted in response.

'My daughter,' Slade supplied in a harsh tone.

She jumped, not having heard him return. Waves of nausea washed over her. If this was his daughter, then somewhere there was a real Mrs Benedict. What did he think he was playing at?

'Not my real daughter, of course,' he supplied as if reading her thoughts. 'Katie was my sister's child. She and her husband were killed in a road accident and Katie was the only survivor.'

Tears blurred Eden's vision. 'Poor little mite. How old was she when they died? I mean, I don't want to pry or anything, but——'

'But you need to know about her in order to play your part,' he cut in before she could finish. He joined her on the couch and lifted the folder from her hands. His expression softened as he studied the photo and she wondered at the change in him. Where was the ruthless, uncaring dictator now?

The expression was gone in an instant, replaced by a hard, cold mask which chilled her to look upon it. 'My sister married against family advice,' he told her. 'When her husband found out that she had no money of her own other than an income from shares I'd given her in my company, what love there was soon died. By then Julie was pregnant with Katie and she stayed for the sake of her child.'

Eden touched his hand lightly. 'You don't have to tell me any more.'

His bleak expression raked her. 'I don't, but I shall, so you know exactly how things are with me. A wife would know, wouldn't she?'

But a real wife, not a play-acting one, she thought painfully. It occurred to her that perhaps there weren't many people he could take into his confidence. With his knowledge of her own personnel file, she was hardly likely to betray his confidence, so he felt safe telling her the facts. With a feeling of emptiness, she nodded.

He linked his hands behind his head and stared at the ocean beyond the window. 'Julie endured it as long as she could but her husband's womanising got too much to ignore. Eight months ago, she telephoned me to say she was leaving him. She and Katie were to stay with me until she decided their future.'

A lump rose in Eden's throat. Was it his sister's experience which had soured him on the idea of marriage? 'What happened?' she asked softly.

'Her husband followed them in his own car, finally forcing them off the road. The roads were wet. Both cars rolled, killing their drivers. Katie was strapped into the back seat of Julie's car and they were able to get her out with only minor scratches.'

'How horrible,' Eden said, wanting to cry. 'Is Katie all right now?'

'She has occasional nightmares about the crash but I've tried to give her as normal a home life as possible. I moved to a house along Nutgrove Beach where she seems to have settled down.'

The area was one of the most exclusive residential parts of Hobart, only a few minutes' drive from the city centre. 'Who takes care of her while you're away from home?'

'Our housekeeper, Ellen. She worked for Julie before the tragedy, and has known Katie since she was born, so it's an ideal arrangement.'

Slade as a family man, with an adopted daughter, was so at odds with her perceptions of him that she felt confused. 'You must love Katie very much to do all that for her,' she speculated.

'That's the trouble,' he said harshly. 'I don't know. I'm still getting used to this father business.'

Eden sat up, hugging her knees close to her chest, unaware of how youthful the pose made her look. 'Why did you decide to adopt her if fatherhood is so unappealing?'

'I didn't say it was unappealing.'

'Your tone did.'

Irritation furrowed his brow. 'You're right. I never wanted the domestic package of a wife and two-point-five children. I had my parents' and Julie's marriage to prove that it doesn't work. But I couldn't abandon my own sister's child.'

Anger rose in Eden, coiling tightly in her chest until she had to say what was on her mind. 'Well, no wonder you don't enjoy fatherhood with that attitude. Katie's probably well aware that she's a duty to you.'

'I've never allowed her to know how I feel.'

'You don't have to. Children know when they're loved and wanted.'

His thunderous expression should have warned her she'd gone too far. 'As far as I'm aware, you're no expert on the subject of marriage and children, unless you lied about them, too.'

'I didn't lie. It was a stupid misunderstanding which got out of hand.' Without telling him the whole story, she couldn't convince him that she had allowed the error to stand out of the purest motives.

'Before coming to work for you, I spent some time as a teacher's aide in a kindergarten. I thought about getting a certificate in early childhood education.' Until the need to earn a living had ruled out the required years of study, she thought ruefully.

'But corporate communications promised bigger rewards and a fast track to the top.' He put his own interpretation on the facts.

She shook her head until her hair haloed around her head. 'It may look that way, but it wasn't why I gave up teaching. I loved being around the little ones. They're so eager to learn, so fascinated by the newness of the world.'

He took in her shining eyes and heightened colour. 'You sound like perfect mother material. When are you going to get off the career ladder and have some of your own?'

Pain knifed through her until she jumped to her feet. 'You don't know what you're talking about,' she threw at him and flung herself through the door into her bedroom, where she leaned against the door, her chest aching with unshed tears.

His fist pounded on the door, sending vibrations shuddering through her. 'Go away,' she shouted.

'Not until you tell me what I said to provoke such an outburst,' he insisted. 'You'd better open up. I'll break the door down if I have to.'

She had no doubt that he meant it and had the strength to back up his threat. Shakily, she opened the door, guarding a narrow opening with her body as if daring him to thrust past her. His shoulder forced the opening steadily wider until she gave up and moved aside. Standing in front of the window, she wrapped her arms around her trembling body.

He came up behind her. Out of the corner of her eye she saw him reach for her, and every nerve-ending tensed. If he touched her, her defences would crumble and she'd be forced to tell him the truth.

Instead, he rested his hands on the back of a chair alongside her, his arms enclosing her without touching her. 'What is it, Eden? What did I say?'

'You didn't say anything. The problem is mine. I can't have children.'

He swore under his breath. 'And I went and put my foot right in it, didn't I?'

'You couldn't know.' Her voice was ragged. This was the last subject she had expected to discuss with him. 'It isn't something I like to advertise.'

'Of course not.' The compassion in his voice caught her by surprise. She hadn't expected him to make allowances for any kind of weakness. She searched his face, seeking at least a trace of the distaste he must be feeling, but found none. 'What's the problem, something physiological?' he asked gently.

She was curiously unwilling to let him think she was less than a whole woman. 'Everything works,' she said, aware that his concern threatened to undermine her shaky defences.

His hand drifted to her cheek, his touch feather-light. 'I wasn't doubting your womanhood,' he assured her. 'You have only to look into a mirror to see the beauty and femininity you possess in breathtaking abundance.'

There was no need. She could see it reflected in his eyes as he regarded her with heart-stopping intensity. Her heart hammered against her ribs. How had they shifted on to such dangerously intimate ground so quickly? It must be the talk of babies which clouded her mind with images of Slade making love to her, the vision so vivid that a gnawing sense of loss filled her. Tears sprang to her eyes.

Slade caught one droplet on the tip of a finger and tut-tutted softly. 'I'm sorry I brought up a sensitive subject. Isn't there anything to be done—test tubes, donor sperm, that sort of thing?'

He had totally misread her tears. For once, they weren't for the child she was capable of bearing but dared not, but for a future which was also beyond her reach.

'There's a ... a genetic problem,' she demurred. Some of the options he'd mentioned were available to her, but it would mean carrying another woman's child. It could never be her own flesh and blood, carrying her own genes. The risk to the child was just too great.

'I've considered the options and they aren't for me,' she said flatly. 'Do you mind if we change the subject?'

'Of course not.' He sounded almost gentle, she thought in astonishment. Damn it, she didn't want him to feel sorry for her. It was easier to fight him when he thought she was as ruthlessly ambitious as himself.

She forced a smile, blinking to clear her blurred vision. 'Well, at least we've achieved our aim. We've gotten to know each other better so our husband and wife act should be much more convincing.'

His eyes hardened as he withdrew his hand. 'It will need to be. Bob Hamilton is checking in tomorrow morning. He's joining us at breakfast.'

Panic started to grip her. 'So early? I was hoping for more time.'

'We still have this evening,' he reminded her. 'I've made reservations in the Oceana Room for seven o'clock.' He glanced at his watch. 'Which just gives us time to change.'

What did one wear to a dinner with one's husband of less than a day? Eden thought when he left her alone. Aware that dressing for dinner was favoured in luxury resorts such as this one, she had included some evening wear in her luggage. But she had imagined herself dining alone or with other single travellers, not with someone as formidable as Slade Benedict.

In the end, she chose a shimmering jumpsuit whose elasticised waist flattered her trim figure. The glitter-trimmed blouson top was suitably dressy while the narrow legs of the trousers emphasised her slim ankles and high-heeled silver evening sandals. In deference to the tropical climate, she used the lightest make-up, dusting her eyelids with silver shadow to complement her metallic drop earrings. Pouting to apply her lipstick, she appraised herself frankly. If she wasn't up to his usual standard in women, he had only himself to blame for choosing her.

When he saw her his blatantly appreciative look dispelled any such doubts. 'Very nice,' he murmured, his eyes warm as he took in the figure-hugging lines of the suit. When he came to the low-cut neckline, she had to resist the urge to tug it closed.

His wolfish smile made it plain that he was aware of her discomfort. 'Don't look so worried; you have my approval.'

'I wasn't aware I needed it,' she snapped.

A provocative gleam glinted in his grey gaze. 'I'm glad to see you're back on form again. I'd hate to think I'd chosen a woman with no spirit.'

He was probably more worried about her impression on his former university classmates than her state of mind, she thought with a flash of anger. How typical.

'You needn't worry. I gave you my word I'd play my part and I shall.'

'You could start by looking a little more loving,' he advised. 'You look as if you'd like to come after me with a meat cleaver.'

She favoured him with a sickly smile. 'How did you guess?'

He tut-tutted softly and stepped closer so she could see the satiny gleam on the lapels of his suit. A dinner-jacket suited him, she thought absently, focusing on his perfectly tied bow-tie as it came nearer and nearer.

'What are you doing?' she demanded, nerves fluttering in her throat.

'Giving you some practice in how to be loving,' he promised, closing the remaining distance between them.

'This isn't part of our...' she managed to get out before his lips closed over hers, muffling the rest of her reminder.

Being kissed by him wasn't part of their agreement, but neither was her uninhibited reaction. Some part of her knew she should be fighting him off with all her strength. Yet the part which welcomed the embrace seemed to be winning.

She had been kissed before, most recently by Joshua, who had managed to convince her he loved her, until the parting came. But nothing had prepared her for the sheer eroticism of Slade's kiss. It sent signals of desire spiralling down her throat, coiling along her backbone, to the very core of her being.

Weakly she clung to his shoulders, her fingers digging furrows into his suit. He had made time to shave and his skin felt like velvet against her cheek.

She inhaled the leathery scent of shaving cream, feeling the slickness on her skin.

'Open your mouth,' he murmured against her lips.

This wasn't supposed to be happening. 'No, I...'

'Eden, obey me.'

Instinctively she did and was swept away by the instant invasion of his tongue, plundering the soft recesses of her mouth. God, he was making love to her with a mere kiss.

When he moved slowly away, she swayed dizzily, trying to absorb the torrent of sensations he had aroused. Then she saw his self-satisfied look as he blotted her lipstick from his mouth with a monogrammed handkerchief. 'You bastard. You knew exactly what you were doing, didn't you?'

'At least you look like a woman who knows the meaning of love.'

He had played her like an instrument and she had allowed it to happen, to the extent of being a willing accomplice. Well, no more!

'You're the one who doesn't know the meaning of love,' she rasped, wiping her mouth with the back of her hand. It felt swollen and bruised. 'I'm sure you know all about *lovemaking*. But as for honest human feelings, I doubt if you have any.'

He tilted an eyebrow at her. 'I have feelings all right, but they're more pragmatic than yours. To me, lovemaking is more real and honest than the romantic myths you subscribe to. You only have to look at my mother and sister to see where romantic love gets you. One is going through a messy divorce from her third husband, and the other is dead at the age of twenty-nine.'

In the evening light, his face was all sharp planes and angles, the look so bleak that she felt chilled in spite of the tropical heat which defied the air-conditioning system. Her heart turned over. She knew only too well how vulnerable past hurts could make a person. The sting of Joshua's rejection was fresh enough to make her guard her family secrets even from Slade.

How much more he had suffered through the loss of his sister and the break-up of his secure family life. 'I'm sorry you feel love is a waste of time,' she offered.

He tilted one ironic eyebrow. 'I didn't say it was a waste of time. Only that it's better to be honest about one's intentions.'

'Total honesty? I have visions of you putting signs up—"For one night only".'

'Very funny. I don't usually need signs, because I ensure that the feelings are mutual.'

What about in my case? she wanted to ask. It would imply that she saw herself as a candidate for his bed, which she most certainly didn't. What did it matter if he preferred physical love to a deeper involvement? It wasn't as if she was planning to get involved with him.

All the same, she couldn't resist asking, 'Don't you find it lonely, just you and your principles?'

He frowned impatiently. 'At least I'll still have my principles come the morning.'

Sorrow for his bleak view of life overwhelmed her own sense of outrage and she fled to the bedroom to repair her make-up. Only thinking of her mother's needs gave her the courage to face

Slade again and accompany him to the hotel restaurant.

She was sure every eye must be upon them as they were shown to one of the best tables. Every time a waiter called her Mrs Benedict, she cringed, but made an effort not to show it in case Slade decided she needed another 'lesson' in loving. How she hated him for taking advantage of her like that.

Or was it herself she disliked for being so compliant? a small voice queried. She *had* enjoyed his kiss, had given herself up to it with all the abandon of which she was capable. What was worse, he knew it and was amused by her response.

Instead of making her task easier, Slade had made it almost impossible, she thought. How could she convince anyone she was a loving wife after this?

CHAPTER THREE

'SLADE, darling. I was hoping to catch up with you here.'

A slight frown creased Slade's smooth forehead as he rose to greet the woman who swept up to their table. Petite in both height and figure, she was stunningly beautiful with china-doll features under a cap of glossy black hair. The hands she extended ended in perfect oval nails which shone with emerald polish to match her vibrant green eyes.

Even before Slade made the introductions, Eden recognised her as Dana Drury, one of Tasmania's best known television personalities and anchor of her own evening current affairs programme.

'Dana, this is Eden Lyle, one of my top researchers,' he explained, drawing Eden into the circle with an expansive gesture.

Dana's cool green gaze rested on Eden for all of ten seconds as she murmured, 'Pleased to meet you. You're here to back up Slade for the conference, I suppose.'

Without waiting for an answer, she returned her attention to Slade. 'Too bad I didn't know you were arriving tonight, or I'd have given my camera crew the slip.' She indicated a table on the far side of the room. The small group around it were watching with obvious interest.

He lifted his shoulders in an apologetic gesture. 'Eden and I have business to discuss in any case.'

Another casual look glanced off Eden before dismissing her again. 'I can hardly accuse you of being a workaholic when everyone knows I'm just as bad. But you will save me a dance later, won't you?'

'I'll join the queue.'

'Save the flattery. I'm a liberated woman, remember?' All the same, she looked pleased as she returned to her table.

Slade sat down again and resumed eating his strawberry soufflé. 'Sorry about the interruption. Dana and I are long-standing friends.'

Dana's flirtatious manner had left Eden in no doubt as to what sort of friends they were. She was disturbed to find that the idea bothered her, although there was no reason why it should. 'I notice you didn't introduce me as your wife,' she commented.

His eyebrows flickered upwards. 'I didn't think you'd want me to. Telling Dana would be like taking out an advertisement.'

'But you don't mind the hotel staff knowing.' The observation was out before she could stop herself.

'It's part of their job to be discreet.' His eyes hardened and the spoon came crashing down into the soufflé dish, making her wince. 'Damn it, Eden, you're giving me the third degree like a real wife. What's going on here?'

She had begun to ask herself the same thing with no convincing answer. 'I'm getting into the spirit of the role,' she excused herself, hoping it was true.

'You're succeeding brilliantly enough to make me glad we're not really married,' he growled.

Annoyance stiffened her spine. He was the one who wanted this charade, not her. 'We can end this any time you say,' she snapped back. 'I'll be only too delighted to go on with my holiday free of any attachments.'

He fixed her with a sharp glare. 'You'd like that, wouldn't you? Is that what this is all about? You're hoping to rile me enough to end the whole thing. Well, it won't work. You gave me your word you'd see it through and I intend to hold you to it.'

She felt tired suddenly, whether with the long flight or the day's surprises she couldn't tell. 'Then you'll have to play your part more convincingly. Bob Hamilton will never believe we're married if you keep snapping at me all the time.'

'On the other hand, it may be even more convincing.'

Sadness welled up inside her. 'You're talking about your parents' marriage, aren't you?'

'All three of them,' he tossed off with apparent insouciance, but she wasn't convinced.

'My father left us when I was sixteen,' she admitted softly. 'It doesn't have to sour you on the whole institution.'

Bitterness twisted his mouth into a thin line. 'As long as you're happy to live in an institution.'

Without consulting her, he ordered coffee and liqueurs, making it plain that the subject was closed. Yet it rankled with him, she sensed.

For her part, she knew only too well the heartache of losing a parent at a young age. She had gone through all the stages of wondering if she was to blame, trying to be a better person, then finally accepting that the fault, if there was one, lay outside herself.

Now she was losing her mother too, by degrees, which made it even more painful. If anyone had a right to be cynical about relationships, she had. Instead, she had clung to the love her family had shared before her father left them. When she thought about her childhood, it was to focus on the happy moments and try to forget the quarrels between her parents, and the sadness once her mother's health began to decline.

She no longer blamed her father for leaving. Peggy had been as much at fault as he had. Never an easy woman to live with, she had perhaps already been suffering the early stages of her illness, unbeknown to her family. Besides, life was too short and precious to hold grudges.

She lowered her eyes against the cynicism in Slade's glare and toyed with her liqueur glass. 'We're poles apart in our thinking. What made you choose me to convince your friend you're married?'

He tossed back his liqueur and set the glass down. 'It was partly convenience. When you told me where you planned to go for your holiday, I had a word with the travel agent to ensure he made this date available to you.'

Momentarily she forgot all about not holding grudges and shot him a look laced with venom. 'You actually manipulated my choice of holiday dates so I'd pick the one which suited you?'

'It suited you as well,' he pointed out, unperturbed by her hostility.

'What would you have done if I hadn't been available at all?'

'Probably showed Bob the photos of Katie I brought with me, and tried to convince him she was my daughter, at home with her mother.'

Her throat dried as she cast about for words to describe his behaviour. 'Do you always use people so callously to get what you want?'

He stirred cream into his coffee before answering. 'You're forgetting, this isn't what I want, it's what Bob Hamilton needs.'

'You'd know best, I suppose?'

His strong fingers closed around the delicate coffee-cup until she feared he might crush it. 'In this case, I do. He needs that money and won't accept it any other way.' He leaned closer, lowering his voice. 'Actually, I'm surprised that you find my methods so disagreeable, considering you use them yourself.'

A mouthful of coffee scalded her throat as she swallowed it too rapidly. 'I beg your pardon?'

'You don't think you were using me when you failed to correct that erroneous employment application?'

'I needed the job.'

'As much as Bob needs this money, although for less laudable reasons, I suspect.'

'Such as my overdose of ambition which you've already mentioned,' she agreed tiredly. To him, they were two of a kind and she had no business criticising his methods. No wonder he chose her to pose as his wife. As he saw it, they were ideally suited.

'Business talks over yet?'

Raising her eyes, she met Dana Drury's feline gaze. 'I've come to claim my dance,' she announced with a sloe-eyed smile at Slade.

He got smoothly to his feet. 'After our heavy discussions, Eden will probably welcome a break.' With exaggerated gallantry, he offered his arm to Dana. 'Will you do me the honour?'

The five-piece band struck up a waltz and Slade swung Dana expertly on to the dance-floor. They made a handsome couple, Eden was forced to concede. Seeing his dark head lowered to catch something Dana was saying, she felt a sharp pang but refused to recognise it as anything like jealousy. She was only pretending to be his wife, and then for a very select audience. She mustn't get too carried away with her role.

Finishing her coffee, she wondered if she should retire to her room. The thought that Slade would be annoyed if she left without his concurrence almost prompted her to go until she remembered that they were sharing a suite. He would have no compunction about waking her to read the riot act if it suited him and he wouldn't let a little thing like a lock stand in his way.

'While our two celebrities are dancing, would you care to join me in a waltz? I'm Len Helliger, Dana's sound recordist,' the man who approached her table explained.

She hesitated. Slade would be even less pleased if she danced with another man. 'I'm Eden Lyle,' she reciprocated. 'I was thinking about turning in.'

His smile was disarming. 'One dance. It isn't even midnight, Cinderella.'

Slade and Dana chose that moment to whirl past. Slade's hand rested lightly against Dana's back where her dress plunged almost to waist level. Dana's head nestled against Slade's shoulder and his head was bent to catch her murmured words. He didn't look in the least like a married man. He wasn't even trying to pretend.

'Sauce for the goose,' she muttered viciously and stood up.

Len Helliger gave her a puzzled look. 'What's that about sauce?'

Her smile was brilliant. 'Nothing. I'd love to dance.'

The band had segued into another slow melody and she moved into Len's arms, which closed around her. 'You're here for the conference?' he asked as their steps blended easily.

'I'm a researcher with Benedict Communications,' she offered, not wanting to lie. 'Slade and I work together.'

His hand slid down her back as he adjusted his hold. 'This is a working trip for me, too. Dana is covering the conference and where she goes, we go.'

Eden smiled up at Len, feeling guilty that she had only agreed to dance to get even with Slade for deserting her with such enthusiasm. 'You must have a fascinating life.'

He bent his head so that his words were contained between them. 'You want the truth? The travel gets boring after a while. All the hotels start to look alike, and we don't get much time for sightseeing. I'd rather be at home with Linda and the kids.'

Startled, she tensed slightly. 'You're married?'

'I hope I didn't give you the wrong impression by asking you to dance. I wasn't coming on to you or anything, but you looked as lonely as I felt.'

Laughter bubbled dangerously near the surface but she suppressed it with an effort. If Slade knew she was dancing with a married man, it would confirm everything he suspected about her supposed lack of scruples.

'It's all right,' she said sincerely. 'I like to dance, too. It was kind of you to ask me.'

He looked relieved. 'Maybe we can do this again some time.'

The music ended and they applauded before Len escorted her back to her table. Slade was already there although there was no sign of Dana. He stood up as they approached and shook hands perfunctorily with Len. 'We've met in the line of duty,' he said coolly.

As soon as Len left them, Slade's expression became thunderous. 'What the hell do you think you're up to?'

The censure in his flashing eyes intimidated Eden but she was damned if she would let him see it. She had agreed to dance with Len partly to prove to Slade that he couldn't have everything his own way. Faced with the consequences, she wondered if it was such a good idea.

'Len invited me to dance and I agreed, since you were preoccupied with Dana,' she said, unable to prevent a note of criticism creeping into her voice.

Something indefinable darkened his expression. 'Jealous, Eden?'

'Hardly,' she denied with a toss of her head. 'Since I don't give a damn what you do, or with whom.'

'Do you apply the same rules to yourself?' he asked in a dangerously soft monotone.

'I don't know what you mean.'

'You don't care that you were dancing cheek to cheek with a married man?'

She hadn't done any such thing, although she understood how it might have looked from Slade's vantage-point. 'It was only a dance. He was lonely for his wife and children.'

'So you took advantage of the opportunity, despite our agreement not to flaunt yourself while you're supposed to be my wife.'

It was too much. Red stained her cheeks as she reached for her evening bag. 'I don't have to listen to this, especially since you demonstrated precious few scruples when you were romancing Miss Drury just now.'

His mocking smile made her want to lash out. 'So it did bother you, Eden.'

'Not at all,' she insisted although the tremor in her voice almost betrayed her. It didn't bother her, did it?

Signing their bill with a flourish, he added a tip and stood up. 'I'll escort you to your room.'

'There's no need. I don't plan to go out raging with the first man I meet,' she assured him defiantly.

Nevertheless, he settled her wrap around her shoulders and kept his hand on her elbow as they negotiated the spaces between the tables to the bank of lifts outside the restaurant. His touch set alarm bells ringing up and down her nervous system and she held herself taut, trying to avoid any additional contact.

What a hypocrite he was, criticising her for enjoying an innocent dance with Len Helliger when he had all but made love to Dana Drury on the dance-floor. It was the typical male double standard, she reasoned furiously. If she really were his wife, he would probably keep her on the shortest leash while enjoying whatever freedoms he wanted for himself.

By the time they reached their suite, her anger was at fever pitch. She wanted to lash out at him, end this farce and catch the first plane home to Tasmania.

But he took the wind out of her sails as soon as the door closed behind them. Snapping on the light, he reached for her wrap and dropped it on to a chair, then clasped her shoulders, turning her so that she was forced to meet his eyes.

'Despite what you're so plainly thinking, my dance with Dana was political rather than personal,' he told her.

It wasn't easy to marshal her whirling thoughts while he held her so close to him. 'If that was political, every woman in the country would vote for you as Prime Minister,' she managed, trying desperately to ignore the warmth of his palms against her shoulders.

He sighed deeply. 'Dana is a powerful member of the media,' he explained carefully. His eyes were dark and compelling. 'I admit we've dated a few times but not seriously. Dana isn't into serious relationships. Her career is too important to her. But it doesn't do to make an enemy of her.'

'I doubt if there's any chance you will,' she said shakily, remembering the closeness she'd witnessed between them.

His eyes gleamed with amusement. 'You are jealous, aren't you?'

Unable to escape from his grasp, she shook her head. 'Of course not. But I resent you having one rule for yourself and another for me.'

'Then I must disabuse you of any such notion. For the duration of this trip, you're my wife and I shall act accordingly.'

A tremor swept through her. 'H-how do you mean?'

'I mean that the only woman I shall hold in my arms or favour with my kisses will be you.'

It wasn't what she'd had in mind and he knew it, she thought, her brain fogged with conflicting emotions. 'Surely w-we needn't keep up the act in private?' she stammered.

He lifted a hand and flicked a strand of hair away from her eyes, the gesture so intimate and proprietorial that the breath caught in her throat. 'Oh, but it is. Tonight has shown me how important it is for us to stay in character all the time, in order to be convincing to Bob.'

Her throat dried and she swallowed convulsively. 'You can't mean we should . . .'

'Make love?' With a gently probing finger, he traced the outline of her mouth, then crooked the finger under her chin so that their eyes met. 'It wouldn't be difficult at all.'

She pulled away from his hand, keeping her head lifted to avoid his touch. 'Yes, it would, for me, anyway. I hate you. If there were any other way of keeping my job or getting another, I'd take it. But you've left me no choice.'

He shook his head in mild reproof, mocking laughter dancing in his grey gaze. 'Eden, Eden, for someone who wormed her way into my life through deceit, you're sometimes a very poor liar. Haven't you heard of body language? While your lips are saying you hate me, your body is telling me the opposite.'

Horrified, she willed herself to stillness, dropping her hands to her sides, then realised she had given herself away yet again. 'It isn't true,' she whispered. The denial sounded hollow even to her own ears. When he'd kissed her earlier, she *had* felt the fierce stirrings of desire even as she told herself she hated him. What sort of devil was he to wreak such havoc with her normally well-ordered feelings? What sort of woman was she to let it happen?

'I see my point is well made,' he observed with a sardonic smile. 'You see, we are two of a kind, Eden. I don't use people any more than you do. We simply make the most of our opportunities. Like the one facing us now.'

Her veins turned molten as heat raced through them, her heart beginning a frenetic tattoo. 'I don't...'

His finger slid down the side of her face in a feather-light caress which sent shock-waves rippling through her. 'Yes, you do, Eden. Deny it all you like but you want what I can give you, what I'd be happy to give you. Don't tell me the thought of a holiday romance never entered your head when you planned this trip?'

She lowered her lashes to hide the revelation in her eyes. She had considered the possibility, however fleetingly, but she'd dreamed of a Prince

Charming to share the delights of a tropical holiday. She had never envisioned someone like Slade Benedict, who demanded far more than she was prepared to give.

'You're wrong,' she said with a decisive shake of her head. 'It isn't what I want at all.'

'Of course not.' His lips brushed her hairline. 'Not this, nor this.' He peppered kisses along the bridge of her nose. 'Nor this.'

He captured her mouth with powerful possessiveness, silencing whatever protestations she might have made. To her horror, she could think of none as her senses reeled from the sheer eroticism of his kiss.

The carefully leashed passion in his touch left her vaguely dissatisfied, and she moved restively against him. Oh, God, he couldn't be right about her, could he? The tendrils of desire coiling up through the centre of her being made her grip his shoulders in agonised acceptance that she did want more, much more.

He made a throaty noise of encouragement as her hands left his shoulders and linked around his neck, her fingernails digging into his flesh in response to the flames of need licking through her.

His hand cupped the small of her back, moulding her to the burgeoning power of his manhood. It was impossible not to be aware of the strength of his need for her, and the discovery convulsed her. She alone had the power to satisfy him now.

Now.

The one word with its transient overtones was enough to stem the rising tide within her. Now might be enough for Slade, but was it enough for her?

With a strangled cry, she pushed at his shoulders, aware of how close she had come to living up to his image of her. She wasn't the ambitious little opportunist he thought she was, yet she had come within a heartbeat of behaving like one.

He sensed the change in her. 'It's all right, Eden. If I'm going too fast for you...'

'It isn't the speed, it's the direction,' she confessed miserably.

A frown darkened his features. 'You can't tell me you didn't want me to make love to you.'

She throttled back a slightly hysterical laugh. 'It wouldn't be the truth if I did.'

'Then you must know I wouldn't put you at risk in any way.'

'I know.' She had never doubted that he would be a considerate lover, protecting her in every way possible. And she had been taking the Pill since her teens, as soon as she understood her mother's illness.

It wasn't those risks that terrified her. It was the moral risk of committing herself to Slade when he had made it clear that all he wanted was to give and receive pleasure, free of any commitment on either side.

'I'm sorry, I just can't,' she said, unable to voice her reasons. Not that he would understand if she did. She could never be as cynical about love as he was.

Even though her future could never include a loving husband and children, however desperately she longed for them, neither could she settle for a purely physical relationship, which was all Slade was offering.

He had released her and she stepped away from him, feeling the need to return to his arms drag at her like actual bonds.

She had a feeling that he sensed her ambivalence, although he probably misunderstood it. 'Are you sure, Eden? I'll only be next door if you change your mind.'

'I won't,' she said, resolve hardening in her although it did little to alleviate the pain of wanting him. 'I'm afraid I'll never be as blasé about love as you are.'

His amused laughter followed her all the way to her room, haunting her along with his barbed parting comment. 'If I didn't know your track record at work, Eden, I'd be tempted to believe you.'

By the time she reached the sanctuary of her bedroom she was shaking from head to foot. The nearness of her escape was still hard to accept. Harder to deal with was her own weakness. This sweeping sense of utter vulnerability was as novel as it was alarming. Against Slade's skilled advances, her meagre defences were useless and, what was more damning, he knew it.

Colour flooded her cheeks as she thought about her unbridled response to his kisses. His shoulders were probably bruised where her fingers had dug into him. She had never behaved so wantonly before. How on earth was she to face him tomorrow, far less carry out the absurd charade that they were man and wife?

He would never allow her to renege on their bargain, she knew. So what was she to do? Still agonising, she changed into her nightie and brushed her hair until it shone. Setting the brush down, she contemplated packing and leaving the hotel before he awoke in the morning. But her return ticket was only valid for her original flights, and she had insufficient funds to pay the substantial difference.

There was only one alternative. She would play her part as agreed, somehow convincing Bob Hamilton that he had won the bet. Then she would insist that Slade put her on a return flight to Tasmania that very day. As far as his friends were concerned, she would be flying home to a sick relative who needed her. It was a flimsy excuse but the best she could think of for now.

One problem still remained. The atmosphere between her and Slade would be strained by what had occurred tonight. If they were to be at all convincing tomorrow, she felt bound to clear the air between them.

Slipping a matching kimono over her nightie, she tied the sash around herself, debating whether to take the time to dress again. It was inviting trouble to confront him in her nightwear after what had so nearly happened. He would think she had come to take up where they left off.

Was it what she wanted? Even now, was she rationalising her behaviour without being consciously aware of it?

A glance in the mirror showed that she was indeed taking a risk. Her colour was hectic and her hair flared in a tawny mane around her head, giving her a wild appearance. In an agony of indecision, she looked from the mirror to her clothes. Slade might be asleep himself by the time she was dressed again.

All she wanted to do was talk to him in a calm, rational manner, she told herself. He wasn't a man who forced himself on to a woman. If she indicated by her demeanour that talk was all she sought, surely there wouldn't be any problems?

Still, it took all of her courage to step out into the darkened living-room. A light shone under his bedroom door so he was still awake, for which she was thankful.

Her fingers closed around the handle of the connecting door but she froze as she heard a knock from outside Slade's bedroom. His footsteps padded across to answer it. 'Dana, this is a surprise.'

There was the sound of tinkling laughter then Dana's sultry response. 'I brought that nightcap I promised you.'

Not waiting to hear any more, Eden fled back to her own room. Frustrated by her, Slade had evidently sought solace elsewhere.

She should be grateful to Dana, she thought grimly. Except that the mutinous rage which flared through her didn't feel like gratitude. Even knowing she was right about Slade's attitude towards love was little consolation.

Later, as she tossed and turned in bed, the reason for her rage came slanting home. It wasn't annoyance with Slade for turning to Dana, it was fear that he might be right about Eden's own feelings towards him. If she stayed, how long would it be before she abandoned her principles and gave in to them?

CHAPTER FOUR

BREAKFAST was served smorgasbord-style beside the lagoon-sized freshwater pool but Eden had no appetite for the sumptuous spread. Butterflies danced in her stomach at the thought of the role she was about to play.

Butterflies? They felt more like World War Two Tiger Moths, she thought. Bob Hamilton was due to join them at any moment and she wasn't nearly ready.

'Cheer up, you're supposed to be a radiant bride,' Slade whispered into her ear. He looked a picture of strength and self-assurance. If only he had been her husband, she could have drawn her courage from him.

'How long are we supposed to have been married?' she asked, fighting a sense of panic. They hadn't discussed anything of importance. What if Bob asked her a question she couldn't answer?

'Let's say we're newly-weds,' Slade supplied, sensing her trepidation. 'It will explain why we're still getting to know each other.'

'I might have known you'd have an answer for everything,' she said bitterly. Judging by his clear-eyed confidence, he had slept well last night. Alone or with Dana Drury? her mind taunted.

His cool glance rested on her. 'If something's bothering you, Eden, you'd better come out with it before Bob gets here.'

60

'It wouldn't do to have him catch the newly-weds in the midst of a quarrel, would it?' she returned.

Fingers of steel closed around her wrist and he drew her close to him across the table. 'Something *is* bothering you. Out with it now.'

A tremor shook her as she met his unrelenting gaze. 'You can't order me around. I'm a liberated woman, too.'

He frowned and she imagined the wheels of his well-ordered mind turning as he placed the phrase. 'Dana,' he said with grim satisfaction. 'You're upset because she came to my room last night.'

She affected a wide-eyed carelessness. 'Me, upset? Why should I care if my *husband* spent the night with another woman?'

His hard glare bored into her. 'Yes, why should you care? Not that she did spend the night, as it happens.'

Not sure whether to believe him or not, she tried to twist free and found herself trapped, unable to escape his searching inspection. You started this, his look seemed to say. Now I'll finish it.

'I don't care,' she denied. 'I wouldn't even have known about it if I hadn't wanted to talk to you last night.'

'You intended to come to my room?'

'To—to talk.'

'So what changed your mind?'

Damn him. Why was he making this so hard for her? Did he want her to spell out what was obvious to both of them? 'I heard Dana arrive. It didn't seem opportune to interrupt your little tête-à-tête.'

He shrugged. 'Pity you didn't. You'd have interrupted a discussion about some educational videos the company is about to make with Dana as the presenter.'

'You really expect me to believe that a beautiful woman like Dana came to your room last night to talk *business*?'

'I don't expect you to believe anything.' His voice cut across her like a whiplash. 'I remind you yet again that the role of wife is a fictitious one. It gives you no rights whatsoever over me.'

As if she needed reminding. 'Thank heavens for small mercies,' she breathed. He had just made it easier to broach the plan she'd hatched last night. 'Since it is fictitious, I think it will be better if we don't keep it up for longer than necessary,' she ventured.

'I suppose you have a solution to that, too?' he drawled.

She toyed with the glass of orange juice in front of her. 'As it happens, I do. After we satisfy your friend about our supposed marriage, I'd like to fly back to Tasmania, giving the excuse of a sick friend needing me.'

'I should have known you'd be ready to twist the truth to suit yourself,' he commented, his eyes dark with derision. 'It is your preferred way of doing things.'

Why did he persist in misreading her motives? 'It's nothing of the sort,' she snapped, unwilling to let him see how much it hurt to have him think so badly of her. 'Since I can't stop you, you'll have to think what you like.'

'As I usually do,' he reminded her. 'You really should try some of the prosciutto and melon. It's excellent.'

She shot him a look which he should have no difficulty in interpreting as a wish that the food might choke him. Fruit juice and toast were all she could manage in her present state of mind.

Slade seemed to have no such problem. He had partaken liberally of the smorgasbord, which included hot and cold cooked food, a cornucopia of tropical fruits, every kind of baked goods, and an array of cereals.

The lanai where breakfast was served was framed by palms, tropical gardens and verdant creepers. The lagoon was crossed here and there by timber walkways and surrounded by potted palms. At any other time, and with anyone other than Slade, she would have felt as if she was in heaven.

As it was, his presence was a constant reminder of how unprepared she was to play her part. Not that she lacked examples if she cared to look around. The resort was popular with honeymooners, and they were easily spotted, being totally involved with one another. It was a far cry from the hostility which must surround the two of them like an aura.

'Are you sure you won't try some melon?' he prompted yet again.

'Oh, for goodness' sake, I'll try it if you insist.' Anything to make him leave her alone.

To her astonishment, he leaned across and placed a segment of fruit nonchalantly between her lips. The touch of his fingers against her mouth was fleeting but jolted through her like a lightning bolt. With an effort, she swallowed the melon, although her throat felt arid, the gesture far too intimate for comfort. 'Why did you do that?'

'It's what honeymooners do,' he said mildly and held out another succulent mouthful. 'Another piece?'

'No—no, thank you.' She was determined not to let him see how badly the gesture had shaken her. Her eyes blurred at the futility of it all.

'Better,' he said on a note of satisfaction. 'Now you look much more like a dewy-eyed bride.'

She favoured him with the sweetest smile she could summon. 'Go to hell.'

His eyes flashed answering fire. 'Undoubtedly you could show me the way.'

Before she could summon a suitably scathing reply, a shadow fell across the table. Above them loomed the largest man she had ever seen. About six feet tall, he was built like a weight-lifter with a thatch of straw-blond hair which fell across vibrant blue eyes. 'Slade, you devil, it's good to see you again.'

A matching grin split Slade's handsome features and he stood up to be enveloped in a bear hug. When they parted, he kept a hand on the big man's shoulder. 'Bob, I'd like you to meet someone very special—my wife, Eden. Eden Benedict, this is the famous Bob Hamilton.'

The shock of hearing her name coupled with his almost robbed her of speech. It was just as well that Bob Hamilton seemed equally taken aback. 'Your what? Good God, man, why didn't you tell me you'd finally tied the knot?'

'We haven't told anyone yet,' Eden said when she could control her voice. At least it was the literal truth. 'I'm delighted to meet you, Dr Hamilton.'

'Bob, please. Any friend of Slade's is practically family to me.' He swung on Slade. 'Your wife? I can't believe it. You used to say you'd cut off your hand sooner than put a ring on it.'

Was Slade's aversion to marriage so well-known? 'People change,' he said good-humouredly.

The big man pulled up a rattan chair which seemed barely large enough to contain him, and put a hand over Eden's. 'You must have something extraordinary to be able to land Slade Benedict. He's about the most gun-shy man around. Or he was.'

'Oh, she's special all right,' Slade surprised her by agreeing.

'You could say I'm the only wife for him,' she contributed, earning a frown of warning from Slade.

Bob gave a booming laugh. 'You realise what this means, old buddy?'

Slade managed to look disappointed and pleased all at the same time. 'I suppose I lose our bet.'

'From the look of you two, it's a bet you're delighted to lose.'

Slade dropped a possessive arm around her shoulders and drew her closer. 'I couldn't be happier with the way it's worked out, Bob.'

The embrace was for Bob's sake, she recognised, but her heart insisted on picking up speed all the same. Breathing became a challenge as warmth from his arm seeped through her filmy cotton blouse. She should pull away or at least allow her tensed muscles to demonstrate her dislike of his touch, but instead she found herself leaning into his embrace, some deeper part of her reluctant to resist. His surprised look flickered to her face.

His husky laugh pierced her trance-like state and she slid free of his hold. 'I don't know about you two, but I'm going back to the smorgasbord,' she announced, keeping her voice level with an effort.

'Perhaps you could bring me some more of that melon,' Slade suggested, his eyes challenging.

It took every ounce of self-control not to throw something at him. 'I doubt if there's any more of the same kind,' she said meaningfully.

He was not to be outdone. 'There's plenty more where that came from.'

'You lovebirds have a language all your own,' she heard Bob say with a laugh as she hurried away, her face fiery. Keeping up the pretence was harder than she'd imagined, only because his experienced touch had a way of breaching her defences. She tried to picture him with Dana but instead of the expected surge of hatred she was surprised by a very different sensation.

This had to stop, she told herself fiercely. Slade was a skilled lover, a virtuoso compared with her amateur experience. She mustn't mistake the chemistry he was deliberately orchestrating between them for anything other than an act to fool Bob Hamilton.

By the time she returned to the table with a plateful of food she had no interest in eating, the two men were deep in conversation, catching up on each other's doings since their last meeting. They rose as she approached the table, until she waved them down again. 'Don't let me interrupt. I'm sure you have lots to talk about.'

About to excuse herself and slip away, she was arrested by Slade's grip encircling her wrist. Inexorably, she was forced back to her seat. 'You can't go yet, darling. Bob was saying how anxious he is to get to know you better.'

'The outback is a little short of beautiful women,' Bob said with a shy smile. Instantly she warmed to the doctor, although her mind was contemplating ways to ensure that Slade choked on his precious melon.

Couldn't he see that the more time she spent with Bob, the greater was the risk that he would suspect the truth?

A sidelong glance showed how unconcerned he was, or else Slade had more faith in her acting ability than she had. There was no alternative but to stay. 'I believe you work with Aboriginal children,' she ventured.

'A group of us medicos run clinics in areas where even the flying doctors find it hard to function, although things are getting better all the time.'

He nodded to Slade. 'Thanks to your husband here—damn, I still can't get used to that idea—I'll be taking back some self-contained video equipment and educational tapes which will be a great help to our isolated communities.'

'You never mentioned such a project,' she reproached Slade. It didn't lessen her personal animosity towards him, but it did prove that he had another side, one she was unlikely to be permitted to share.

He gave a faint smile. 'It's no big deal. Part of my reason for attending this conference is to ex-

plore the potential of video education to bridge
Australia's vast distances.'

Bob winked at her. 'So you see, the money I won
from our bet will be put to good use in the outback.'

'I should congratulate you on winning,' she said,
then hesitated, wondering if congratulations were
appropriate.

'It's OK,' he said, sensing her discomfort. 'I'm
not bemoaning my single state. I'm too busy with
fund-raising and running the clinics. Besides, there's
this nurse in the flying doctors...'

'You mean if I'd only waited I'd have won the
bet?' Slade said in mock-despair.

Bob nodded amiably. 'There's nothing definite
between us, but you never know. Anyway, you
couldn't keep a beauty like Eden waiting. Someone
else might come along and snap her up.'

'Not much chance of that,' Eden admitted, her
smile self-deprecating.

Fortunately, Bob misunderstood. 'It was Slade
or no one, right?'

'He did rather sweep me off my feet. One minute
I was fancy-free, and the next I was Mrs Slade
Benedict,' she said, enjoying Slade's cautionary
look which was quickly masked.

His eyes flashed a brilliant warning as he rose to
his feet. 'I think that's enough for one morning.
We have a conference session to attend.'

'But Bob hasn't had any breakfast yet.'

'I ate on the plane.' The doctor uncoiled from
the chair. 'How will you spend your morning,
Eden?'

'I have some letters and postcards to write so I'll
find plenty to do.' Such as packing, she added to

herself. Now that she had done her duty, surely Slade wouldn't expect her to stay any longer?

'Then we'll see you at lunch,' Slade said smoothly, giving no sign that he remembered her plan to leave today. 'Enjoy your morning, darling.' Before she could prepare herself, he claimed her mouth in a swift but thorough kiss which left her momentarily speechless.

As he stepped away, her hand went to her mouth in stunned surprise. The kiss had been for Bob's benefit but her throbbing response didn't seem willing to recognise the fact.

She was glad that Slade didn't require her presence at the conference this morning because she badly needed some time to herself. The feelings he aroused in her were too confusing, for a start. Knowing that it was all an act on his part didn't seem to help.

Why did he have to involve her in his wretched charade? It wasn't fair of him to ruin the first holiday she'd had in years. She could have survived without the luxuries which surrounded her, she thought, surveying the elegant furnishings. The cost to her peace of mind was simply too high.

Frustrated, she got out some hotel stationery and composed a letter to her mother which the nurses would read to her. Needless to say, Slade didn't rate a mention. Then she wrote a postcard for Fiona, addressing it to the nurse's family address in Scotland. Those duties done, she changed into her swimsuit and headed for the hotel pool. By the time she had swum several lengths of the serpentine waterway, she felt better and returned to the suite to dry her hair and style it in time to meet Slade for lunch.

Her choice of a flutter-sleeved dress with blouson top, fitted waist and gathered skirt was more romantic than she would have wished, but it was the most suitable dress she had with her.

With her hair dried and fluffed out around her head, she was ready to face Slade again, telling herself it was the last time she would be forced to pose as his wife. By this afternoon she would be on her way home to Tasmania.

'Over here, Eden,' Bob's booming voice greeted her as she scanned the sea of tables occupied by the conference attendees.

'Did you have a good morning?' she asked when she made her way over to him. There was no sign of Slade.

He grimaced. 'Too many speeches for a country doctor's liking, but your better half did a good job with his keynote address.'

Automatically she glanced around. 'Where is Slade?'

'He was buttonholed by some of the delegates wanting to pick his brains. He'll be along soon.'

She should be thankful for his absence but Eden was oddly conscious of the empty chair beside her. Her edginess made Bob smile. 'You newly-weds hate being out of each other's sight, don't you?'

'I didn't know it showed,' she confessed. Bob would be surprised if he knew that what she missed most about Slade was the sparks of constant antagonism which somehow added spice to every encounter.

'It shows all right,' Bob acknowledged. 'I've never seen Slade so smitten with anyone as he is with you.'

How well Slade must have played his part to convince his old friend so thoroughly. 'You must have known each other a long time,' she said to deflect his interest in their make-believe love match.

'We went to high school together, then university. I wanted to be a professional footballer while Slade swore he'd end up running a harem. Now look at us. The only ball I play is in a dusty outback paddock, and Slade's become a one-woman man.'

Slade might be a one-woman man for the purpose of this trip, but he wouldn't stay that way—if he even lasted the trip, she thought, remembering Dana Drury's late-night visit to his suite.

Speak of the devil! 'It is Dr Hamilton, isn't it?' a distinctive voice cried as the lady herself arrived at their table. 'Let's see, it was the bicentennial programme I did on "men with a mission".'

Bob gave an embarrassed grin. 'I'm surprised you remember one interview when you do so many, Miss Drury.'

'I have a memory like an elephant when it concerns the programme,' she assured him. 'Maybe we can get together for an update during the conference.'

'You should do something about the new educational videos Benedict Communications is producing,' he offered.

Dana patted his shoulder. 'I know all about them. I'll be doing some of the presentation.'

'I'm delighted to hear it. They'll be even more popular,' he boomed, earning a gratified look from Dana.

Eden kept her head lowered, hoping that Dana would overlook her presence at the table, but Bob had no such qualms. 'Here's your real story,' he said, grasping Eden's hand as she stifled a horrified gasp. 'Have you met Slade's new wife?'

For a moment the room went still but Eden felt sure it was only her overworked imagination. She didn't imagine the intensity of Dana's interest, however. 'His wife?'

'You bet. Australia's most eligible bachelor is a married man at last.'

Dana's smile was brittle and didn't quite reach her emerald eyes. 'Now that *is* news.'

'We're hoping to keep it quiet,' Eden said with a furious look at Bob. He was so delighted with the news that he wanted to share it with the whole world, but it was the last thing Slade would want.

'A secret marriage and a hideaway honeymoon— this is a scoop,' Dana went on as if Eden hadn't spoken. 'I suppose it was an office romance?'

'Perhaps you should ask Slade for the details,' she attempted.

'I shall indeed,' Dana said drily. 'He and I go back a long way so he owes me an explanation.'

Eden wondered whether Dana was referring to the story or to her own relationship with Slade. Either way, he would have some explaining to do when Dana caught up with him. Serve him right for starting this ridiculous deception.

Nausea raced through her. This whole thing was getting out of hand and the sooner it was over the better. 'Excuse me, I'll be back in a moment,' she said, leaving Dana standing as she made her way to the ladies' room.

Splashing cold water on to her wrists and forehead made her feel a little better. She was repairing her make-up when the door opened and Dana came in. 'If it isn't *Mrs* Slade Benedict,' she said with exaggerated emphasis.

Checking to ensure that they were alone, Eden gave her an imploring look. 'Don't say anything about this to anyone, please? We really do want to keep it quiet for now.'

Dana's smile was conspiratorial. 'I understand. You could have knocked me over with a feather when Bob Hamilton made his announcement.'

'I'm sorry if it was a shock to you.'

'That's the understatement of the year. Not once yesterday did Slade hint that he was married.'

Eden felt a flash of compassion for the other woman. How must she feel now if she had allowed Slade to make love to her last night, believing he was free to do so? It was tempting to tell her the reason for the deception and ask for her help in keeping it from Bob. But the secret wasn't Eden's to share. Slade would have to make his own peace with Dana.

She turned towards the door. 'Thanks for being so understanding.'

A grim smile lightened Dana's eyes as she slashed lipstick across her full mouth. 'There's nothing to thank me for, Eden.'

Maybe she had underestimated the other woman, Eden thought as she made her way back to the table. Dana had to be tough to survive in such a competitive industry, but she seemed to have a heart as well.

Neither she nor Bob mentioned the incident to Slade when he finally joined them. Both men were too busy discussing the conference. Eden was happy to be left out of the conversation and ate her grilled barramundi in thoughtful silence.

After the meal, Bob left them to attend another session and Slade offered to escort Eden back to their suite. 'It isn't necessary. It won't take me long to pack,' she insisted when Bob was out of earshot.

'There's no need to pack. You aren't leaving yet.'

'But we agreed . . .'

'You suggested a plan. I don't recall agreeing to it.'

When they were alone in their suite, she shook off his arm. 'I've done what you asked. Bob is convinced we're married. What more do you want from me?'

'It's what I can do for you this time, Eden,' he explained, startling her into silence. 'I don't intend to let you go home until you've had a proper holiday.'

'As your wife,' she second-guessed him.

'Granted, you must continue to play the part, but is it so onerous? I gather you had a pleasant enough morning while I was at the conference.'

Her mouth set into a mutinous line. 'I suppose so.'

'Then why not plan more of the same?' The knuckles of his right hand grazed her cheek. 'I'm not such an ogre that I would deny you the holiday you obviously need.'

But only on his terms. 'It seems I have no choice but to stay, since I can't change my return ticket and you won't make other arrangements,' she said flatly.

'Then it's settled.' Dismissing the subject, he poured a drink, shrugged when she refused one, and stretched out on a couch to study some notes from the morning session.

Alone in her room, she closed the blinds and lay down, lulling herself to sleep by counting the ways she would like to get even with him.

More exhausted than she realised, she slept until almost dinnertime and was roused by the sound of the television set as Slade turned on the evening news. Rubbing sleep from her eyes, she stumbled out into the living-room to find the screen filled with the image of Dana Drury.

'Tonight's stories include the latest from Com-Con, the communications technology conference being held on the Sunshine Coast, and an update on Queensland tourism. But first a round-up of snippets about the rich and famous.'

Eden went cold from head to foot, hoping desperately that she was still asleep and dreaming. Dana wouldn't, would she? She hadn't actually promised not to reveal her scoop, Eden saw now, finally recognising the polite evasions which she had foolishly taken as assurances.

'Hottest news is also from Com-Con,' Dana continued. 'Australia's most eligible bachelor has changed his status at long last. Slade Benedict is reported to be combining the conference with his honeymoon.'

The room whirled about Eden and she grabbed the back of a chair for support. Dear heaven, Slade would think this was her doing. His attention was riveted to the small screen but his clenched hands and the rigid set of his jaw betrayed his fury.

Her tension grew as Dana summarised Slade's professional background and his meteoric rise to the ranks of Australia's richest men. As she talked, a strange glow crept over Eden. She recognised it as a thrill of pride, something she'd never felt for Joshua, although he was successful enough in his own way. This was different. She wanted to tell the world that this was her husband they were talking about.

Suddenly her hand flew to her brow. What was the matter with her? She was reacting as if Slade were really her husband when the publicity about their fictitious marriage was hardly cause for rejoicing.

'Little is known about the bride, the former Eden Lyle, a researcher with the Benedict organisation,' Dana went on. 'But she is beautiful, as are all the Benedict women. Or should I say as *were* all the Benedict women when Slade was still fancy-free? In our next story...'

Eden jumped as Slade snapped off the television set and turned on her. 'I hope you're satisfied now.'

'It wasn't my doing, Slade.'

His eyebrows arched in disbelief. 'Oh, no? Then you didn't plan this to get even with me for denying you the promotion and spoiling your holiday?'

'No, I didn't. What on earth would I have to gain?'

'Do I need to spell it out? The potential for blackmail is perfectly obvious.'

Blackmail? She almost choked on the unfairness of this thought. Her momentary fantasy of marriage to him seemed even more foolish than before. 'Blackmail never entered my head,' she denied. 'You make it sound as if I *want* to be known as your wife.'

A challenging gleam lit his dark gaze. 'Don't you, Eden?'

Even as she shook her head, denial pulsed through her mind. In other circumstances, she could have been very much attracted to Slade. He had a way of dominating her thoughts when she least expected it. Now, for instance. He had accused her of betraying his trust, yet she could still be distracted by his searching look which seemed to see into her soul, stripping bare her deepest yearnings.

The moment lasted only seconds yet awareness leapt between them like a bolt of lightning. He knew, she thought forlornly. Recognising the attraction she was powerless to conceal, he had put his own interpretation on it.

'You're wrong,' she said in an undertone, not entirely sure which error she meant to correct.

'Then you didn't talk to Dana Drury?'

'Yes, I did, but not in the way you think.'

He folded his arms across his broad chest. 'Just what *did* you tell her?'

'Nothing about us. I gave you my word.'

'And I trusted you, Eden. You know how much this means to Bob Hamilton, or I wouldn't have involved you.'

'And I didn't let you down.'

'Then how did she come by the information?'

Before she could explain, the telephone shrilled through the suite. As he reached for it she turned away but his fingers curled around her wrist. 'Stay, we haven't finished yet,' he said.

Stay and be pilloried for something she hadn't done, she interpreted. Her efforts to squirm free were futile, his strength being more than a match for hers. She could do nothing but wait until he finished his call.

In the interval, she studied his bent head as he concentrated. A lock of dark hair fell across his eyes, making her want to brush it back until she realised what she was thinking. Heat flooded through her. She had denied wanting to be his wife, but the attraction was too strong to deny.

It was probably the result of sharing such close quarters, but it disturbed her all the same. She wasn't ready for a repeat of her experience with Joshua, and already Slade loomed far too large in her thoughts. He stirred a bewildering variety of responses in her. She couldn't be starting to care for him, could she? No! She'd had more than enough of unrequited love.

His expression was bleak as he set the phone down. He had released his grip on her arm and now he raked long fingers through his hair.

'What is it?' she asked, bracing herself for more bad news.

'That was my housekeeper, Ellen. My adopted daughter, Katie, heard about us on TV in Hobart and she's broken-hearted. After losing her parents in the car crash, she's convinced she's lost me too, to you.'

CHAPTER FIVE

'DIDN'T you explain that it's all a terrible misunderstanding?'

'I might have done if her uncle hadn't called Katie moments after the broadcast. Katie thinks she's the only one who didn't know.'

Eden's hand went to her mouth. 'Poor little girl. She must feel terrible.'

'You should have thought of her when you talked out of turn to Dana.'

With a whimper of distress, she tore herself away from him and went to the railing, staring blindly at the endless expanse of golden beach. When she turned, keeping the railing protectively at her back, her eyes streamed tears of anger and frustration but she dashed them away with the back of her hand. 'Knowing what you think of my honesty, I don't expect you to believe me, but I didn't betray your confidence.'

His expression was cold and unrelenting. 'Then how did Dana get hold of the information?'

'Someone else introduced me as your wife at lunch,' she said in a low voice, unwilling to identify Bob. He didn't know the damage he was doing.

Slade quickly made the connection. 'Bob?' When she nodded he slammed a fist into the palm of his hand. 'Damn, I should never have left him alone during the break.'

'He's rather large to bind and gag,' she said shakily.

The faintest trace of amusement dispelled the bleakness in his expression. 'You have a point. Not that it changes the basic problem.'

'Surely Katie will understand when you can explain it to her face to face?'

His frown deepened. 'Ordinarily, I would. But Katie isn't an ordinary nine-year-old. She's only now getting on to an even keel emotionally after losing both her parents. I'm all she has in the world.'

'I can see why this news hit her so hard,' Eden observed. She spread her hands in a gesture of futility. 'I'd do anything to put things back the way they were before all this happened.'

His dark lashes lowered over feral eyes. 'Would you, Eden?'

At the raw challenge in his voice, the fine hairs on the back of her neck lifted. 'Of course I would. Half of Australia now believes I'm your wife. How am I going to explain that I'm not?'

'Perhaps you won't have to.'

Her wide eyes reflected her shock as she saw where he was leading. 'No! You can't mean us to continue this...this farce indefinitely? I can't, I won't. It's utter madness.'

Utter madness to have considered an alliance with him in the first place, even for a worthwhile cause, far less think of extending it beyond their agreement. Yet she saw from his determined look that it was what he had in mind.

He prowled closer, his movements more panther-like than ever. Involuntarily, she shrank from the hand he raised to her cheek. 'Why not? I don't believe you dislike me as much as you want me to think. The truth is too transparent in your response. Even now, as you shrink away, your eyes invite me closer.'

'Some men don't know how to take no for an answer,' she flung at him. How she hated him for his perception. Around him, she felt impossibly vulnerable, and he knew it. With his callous attitude towards marriage, how long would it be before he took all she could give, leaving nothing behind?

'It would be an ideal marriage,' he went on as if she hadn't interrupted. 'Through me, you'd have that fast track to the top which is so dear to your heart, while I'd get a reprieve from hordes of matchmaking hostesses.'

Doubtless being free to continue his bachelor lifestyle without hindrance, she thought sourly. 'Aren't you forgetting Katie?' she queried.

His eyes glinted. 'Katie would be gaining something she badly needs—a mother. Think of it, Eden. Katie could be the child you're unable to have for yourself. Instead of losing a father, she gains two loving parents.'

He had it all worked out, she thought bleakly. Katie was an unfair weapon. She would love to be a mother to the child she'd glimpsed in his photograph. But the price was too high. 'You can't make me marry you,' she whispered.

His breath was a soft wind against her cheek. 'I've never had to force myself on any woman. I think you want it too, but you're too stubborn to admit it.'

Her indrawn breath matched the movement of his head as his lips found hers. A low groan escaped her throat as she acknowledged the truth. She did want him, wanted much more if she was brutally honest. How could she dislike him so thoroughly, yet glory in his touch? It didn't make any sense.

The railing pressed into her, bending her backwards as he trailed kisses along the plunging neckline of her dress until his tongue tantalised the cleft between her breasts, which felt hot and swollen. The peaks were so sensitised that the faint friction of her bra made her want to cry out.

Her fingers twined in his hair as his scalding body pressed against her. 'Say it, Eden,' he urged. 'Tell me no and it will end here. You have only to say the word.'

'I . . .' Words refused to force themselves past the lump engorging her throat. She knew she should say it. He was proposing a coldly logical arrangement which had nothing to do with love. Yet she couldn't make herself end it. His touch set her senses reeling in a way she had never experienced before.

The thought of sharing the future with him spun through her mind like a golden fantasy, a dream she had believed was forever beyond her reach. With Slade, she could have his companionship, even if not his love. And his daughter, Katie, would be the child she dared not have.

'I can see that the benefits are starting to dawn on you,' he said, stepping away from her. Flattening both hands against the railing, he stared out to sea.

'I wasn't thinking of any benefits, at least not in a material sense,' she denied. 'It doesn't have to be entirely cold and logical, does it?'

Telling herself that she was foolish to expect more than he was prepared to give, she held her breath all the same as she waited for his answer.

'Logic is more enduring than love, at least in my experience,' he stated grimly.

A pang shot through her. How terrible to have to live with such a cynical view of the world. 'All marriages don't end like your parents' and your sister's,' she reminded him.

'Tell that to your father,' he retorted, then relented as he caught sight of the pain contorting her face. 'I had no right to say that; I'm sorry.'

'But it is true,' she acknowledged with difficulty. Then she sighed. 'Perhaps your way is better.'

'Then say you'll marry me. We could be good for each other, Eden. This trip has shown me that it can work.'

He was only proposing marriage for his daughter's sake and to simplify his own life, she thought dully. But the tantalising vision of herself as his wife, being a mother to a poor orphaned child who had already captured Eden's heart in her photograph...the prospect tugged at her emotions. There was really only one answer she could give.

'Yes,' she whispered.

'Excellent.' He sounded like a man who had just concluded a particularly satisfying business deal. All at once, the enormity of what she had just agreed to threatened to overwhelm her and she swayed.

His arm came around her, steadying her. 'Are you all right?'

With his arm tight around her, she was more than all right. His strength flowed into her, overcoming all doubts. 'I'm fine, just a bit overcome,' she assured him.

The concern in his expression warmed her. 'It's understandable, in the circumstances. Do you feel up to discussing some of the details?'

'Yes, of course.' There was no point in putting it off. 'I imagine, for Katie's sake, the ceremony should take place as soon as possible,' she assumed.

He nodded. 'Since the world thinks we're already married, it can't be too soon. Keeping it out of the media will be easier here than in Tasmania, so I'll fly Katie and Ellen to the Sunshine Coast as soon as the conference is over.'

'How will you explain a wedding ceremony to Katie, when she thinks we're already married?' she asked, bemused by his rapid-fire decision-making. No wonder he was so successful in the business world.

'It's a good question. Do you have any ideas?'

It was a logical enough question but she couldn't help wondering if he asked it because he thought she was more experienced in deception, given the fiasco over her job application. It seemed as if that one mistake was going to haunt her for a long time to come.

'We could tell Katie that we're having a second wedding ceremony to give her the chance to attend,' she thought aloud. 'Lots of people are married in civil ceremonies, then affirm their vows elsewhere later on.'

He leaned forward, his gaze roving over the spectacular view. After several tense moments, he looked sideways at her. 'It's a sensible solution and is bound to satisfy Katie. But will it be enough for you?'

'I'm not sure what you mean.'

'My sister, Julie, believed that a wedding day is the most important day of a woman's life. Will you be happy with a quiet ceremony attended only by Katie, Ellen and my mother?'

Since it wasn't a real commitment, it shouldn't matter but she was oddly touched by his unexpected consideration. 'It will be fine,' she assured him. 'I'm glad your mother will be able to attend.'

'It's a shame you have no relatives to invite.' On her employment application form, the one responsible for this whole mess, she had left the space for next of kin blank.

Her vision blurred. Her mother couldn't have made the journey to the Sunshine Coast in any case, and there was no one else she cared to ask. Perhaps she should tell him about her mother, while there was still time to change their plans. The thought that he might want to change them once he knew made the words stall in her throat and the moment passed.

'Then it's settled,' he said. 'We'll be married the day after the delegates fly home.'

It was less than a week away, she counted, fighting a surge of panic. Was she doing the right thing, commending her future to this man, knowing how he felt about love? Yet wasn't it for the best? With her genetic inheritance, she couldn't expect real love. This way, by the time she knew her fate, the marriage would have served its purpose. Katie wouldn't need them any more and Slade probably wouldn't need her. It was a surprisingly painful thought, but one she might as well accept.

'There is one more thing,' he said, startling her out of her reverie.

Apprehensively she turned large eyes to him. 'What is it?'

'As your husband, I will require complete fidelity.'

'But the same doesn't apply to you?'

His jaw tightened on clenched teeth. 'You shall have mine as long as you remain faithful to me.'

Shock-waves eddied through her. 'It sounds as if you intend our marriage to be a real one.' The observation came out as tremulously as she felt.

'It will be real,' he said silkily, the promise in his tone turning her bones to water. 'Did you doubt it?'

'But I ... we ... it's for Katie's sake, surely?' she stammered. The very thought of sharing the physical side of marriage with him painted vivid mental images, exploding through her mind.

What would it be like to be the total focus of his desire, to invite his possession and to possess him in turn with the silken bonds of shared passion? It was so much more than she had bargained for when she'd agreed to marry him that a retraction hovered on her lips. At the same time, she was conscious of a rising sense of excitement which stayed her tongue.

'This has nothing to do with Katie,' he countered, 'and everything to do with what we feel and want. I don't doubt that you want me as much as

I want you, even if it can't lead to children,' he finished, his voice a low murmur, redolent with erotic potential.

Her limbs felt weak and it was as well she had the railing to support her. Gradually anger rose in her. 'This is perfect for you, isn't it? You get a mother for your adopted child, and a marriage which doesn't cramp your style one bit. Right down to sex on demand.'

His husky laugh caught her by surprise, inflaming her anger even further. 'I don't think I'll have to do much demanding, my dear. I rather think that will be your role.'

'Go to. . .' She stopped herself in time, recalling his belief that she would lead the way. 'I'll never ask you to make love to me, so don't hold your breath.'

He shook his head sadly. 'Such a waste of passion. Shouldn't you save it for our wedding night?'

If she didn't kill him beforehand, she thought savagely. It was an unlikely thought for a bride to have, less than a week before the ceremony. But then everything about this marriage was unlikely, especially her acceptance.

'I'm so glad you married my son. I'd given him up as a lost cause,' Marian Benedict commented as they shared coffee at the poolside restaurant a few days later.

Like everyone else, Slade's mother believed they were already married, the forthcoming ceremony being a formality for Katie's sake. Eden hated deceiving the older woman, whom she already liked, but there was no alternative. In any case, it would soon be the truth.

Talking about her son was one of Marian's favourite diversions, her prospective daughter-in-law had discovered. As the veteran of three marriages herself, she had left Eden at a loss as to what to call her. 'Call me Marian, my dear, even Slade does,' she urged when they were introduced. 'I reverted to Benedict for his sake but he doesn't appreciate it. I should jolly well have hyphenated all three married names and made him use them.'

Marian was a warm, forceful woman and it wasn't hard to see where her son got his domineering behaviour from. Already today his mother had dragged Eden to every boutique on the coast in search of the perfect wedding outfit. It was all Eden could do to steer Marian away from the traditional white wedding gowns which drew her like a magnet. Considering the nature of Slade's proposal, it would be a travesty.

Marian had misinterpreted her reluctance. 'White doesn't mean what it used to, my dear. I wore white at my last wedding and nobody was affronted. Be thankful you and Slade have a normal, healthy relationship. If he's anything like his father, he'll be quite a handful.'

Colour flooded Eden's cheeks. She wasn't used to mothers speaking about their sons this way, but then she had never met anyone quite like Marian Benedict. 'Why did you and Slade's father separate?' she felt emboldened to ask.

Marian swept a crocodile-patterned jacquard dress off a rack and held it up for Eden's inspection. 'He was too preoccupied with business to have time for his family. The only time I really saw him was in bed.'

Slade's mother thought Eden was already well acquainted with the sexual side of married life, she realised uncomfortably. 'Maybe that's why Slade tries to keep a balance between work and home life,' she observed.

'He's only a one-woman man,' Marian confided, leaning close to Eden. 'Which is more than I could say for his father.'

Eden's paleness betrayed her shock. 'I'm sorry to hear it.'

'So was I, but men will be men—at least, some of them will.' She laughed self-deprecatingly. 'I wasn't supposed to know about his womanising, although I'm sure Slade did. Even as a teenager, he went to great lengths to protect me from the truth.'

'He must love you a great deal.' Eden's mind whirled. How much had Slade inherited from his father? He had insisted on her fidelity but would his own end with protecting her from the truth, as he had done with his mother?

'He does, but not as much as he loves you,' Marian said with a smile. 'I've seen how he looks at you when you're unaware of it. The fact that you actually got him as far as the altar speaks for itself.'

It did, but not in a language which Marian would understand. Despite her many marriages, she was a romantic at heart, Eden was discovering. She would be appalled that Slade was marrying Eden for his own convenience, not out of love at all.

When Eden shook her head, Marian replaced the taupe dress on the rack and took out another. This time, Eden couldn't withhold a gasp of delight. 'It's gorgeous.'

The dress was a luminous silk chemise in palest rose trimmed with iridescent sequins and tiny seed beads. The sleeves and hem were fringed with leaves tipped with sequins. 'You don't think it's too much, do you?' she asked Marian anxiously.

'Definitely not. It will be my wedding gift to you,' she insisted. 'Try it on, quickly.'

The dress fitted perfectly, as Eden knew instinctively that it would. The slim lines hugged her trim figure and the woven silk lining whispered against her skin. A tiny matching cloche nestled against her hair, the sequins reflecting the lights the tropical sun had bleached into her tresses.

'You look breathtaking, my dear. We'll take it,' she said to the bemused designer, before Eden could utter a word.

'You really shouldn't have,' she told Marian on the drive back to the hotel, their hire car piled high with packages. Katie was due to arrive that afternoon in the company of Slade's housekeeper, Ellen. For the little girl, they had chosen a romantic ruffled gauze blouse and skirt in a complementary rose-pink. The blouse had a jewel neckline and three-quarter sleeves with ruffled cuffs, while the skirt was full and edged in tiers of ruffles. For a child, it was a dream outfit.

Apprehension began to take hold of Eden as they neared the hotel. 'What's Katie like?' she asked Marian.

Marian bit her lip. 'She was the happiest, most outgoing child. Since my daughter...since the tragedy, she's been more subdued. But she's still delightful company.'

'What if she doesn't like me?'

Marian's hand clasped hers. 'It may take time, but she's bound to fall in love with you just as Slade and I did.'

It was ironic to think that Katie's reaction might be similar to Slade's. Far from falling in love with her, he had accused her of dishonesty and opportunism. She hoped she would fare better with his daughter.

Slade had gone to the airport to meet Katie and Ellen, and was due to return at any moment. Eden finished her coffee and excused herself to return to her room to freshen up.

'I don't know why. You look lovely,' Marian insisted, but waved her away with an understanding smile.

In her room, Eden paced up and down, her nerves stretched to the limit. There was an ache around her heart for the little girl. They had so much loss in common. How she wanted Katie to like her.

Tension throbbed through her as a key grated in the lock and the door opened to admit Slade. 'Katie and Ellen are settling into their rooms. They'll be along in a few minutes,' he informed her.

'How do I look?' she asked, patting a strand of hair into place with a nervous gesture.

His dark gaze came to rest on her. 'You look lovely, as always. Katie is sure to adore you.'

Which was more than could be said of him, she thought with a surge of disappointment. Yet she knew better than to expect sweet nothings. It was precisely because he thought she didn't expect them that he had proposed to her.

A timid knock on the door heralded Katie's arrival. At Slade's command, she was shepherded into the room by a tall, angular woman with black hair pulled back from her face. Her graceful movements suggested she might have once been a dancer. 'This is Ellen Sylakas,' Slade introduced his housekeeper.

They murmured greetings.

'And this is my daughter, Katie. Katie, this is Eden.'

The little girl had the makings of beauty with a heart-shaped face, luminous dark eyes fringed with velvet lashes, and a rosebud mouth which unfortunately was twisted into a pout. 'Hello,' she said grudgingly.

At the sight of her, Eden's heart turned over. A love she hadn't known she possessed welled up inside her. She could be a mother to this lost little girl, she knew she could, if Katie would only give her a chance.

Eden held out her hand, which was studiously ignored. 'Hello, Katie. Did you enjoy your flight?'

The little girl shrugged. 'It was OK. I've been in lots of planes before.'

How worldly-wise she was, and how vulnerable, despite her veneer of toughness. 'I'm glad.' Her eyes went to Ellen for confirmation. 'Have you had lunch yet? We could go down to the pool.'

'I had a sandwich on the plane and I'm too tired to swim. I'd like to go back to my room.'

Slade ruffled the child's dark curls. 'Off you go, pet. You and Eden will have plenty of time to get to know each other.'

Katie had her back to the room so Eden could only hear her muffled words. 'Too bad.'

With an apologetic smile, Ellen escorted her charge out of the suite. When the door closed behind them, Eden sank on to a couch and let her head drop back, her posture mirroring her sense of defeat. 'She doesn't like me.'

'She doesn't like anyone very much at the moment. My reception wasn't much better.'

'It's natural for her to feel betrayed.' Eden knew only too well how bereft she had felt when her father left them. For Katie there wasn't even the hope that he might return.

The tears which shimmered in her voice brought him to her side. 'What about you, Eden? Do you feel betrayed? This isn't what you wanted from love and marriage, is it?'

'It's what we agreed to,' she said shakily.

'And I intend to hold you to it. So I hope this little setback isn't going to cloud your judgement.'

He called Katie's obvious hostility a little setback? The man had a heart of stone. 'I wouldn't dream of it,' she said, her voice sounding brittle. She had another reason for wanting this to work now, and her name was Katie.

Never had Eden seen a child in such need of love, yet so determined not to trust herself to it ever again. Somehow she would break through that barrier, she vowed to herself. Not even Slade's aloofness would be allowed to stop her.

'See that you don't. As my mother will doubtless tell you, I'm better to have as an ally than an enemy.'

A shiver rippled through her at the thought of opposing him. It wasn't something she would do lightly and she had no doubt that retribution would be swift and unpleasant. But she had to start as she meant to go on.

'There's something you may as well know about me, too. I don't respond well to threats.'

He dropped on to the couch beside her. 'What do you respond well to? Coercion, perhaps?'

Pulling her hard against him, his mouth found hers with unerring accuracy, forcing her lips apart before she could think to clamp them shut. Warmth invaded her limbs, turning them liquid, as he deepened the kiss. There was nothing she could do but respond.

Her georgette dress had ridden high up her tanned thighs and the heat of his hand against her skin was so intimate and possessive that her heart thudded in response.

'Oh, God, Eden, I want you so much.' The admission came with astonishing suddenness, as he buried his face in the curve of her neck, his fingers tangled in her hair.

'Yes, yes,' she breathed, caught up in a maelstrom of sensations which threatened to sweep her away. It was going to be all right. He was going to be her husband and they would work it out somehow.

His lips found her throat and the soft curve of her jaw, trailing kisses over every inch of her satiny skin until he returned to her mouth. Instead of reclaiming it, he painted teasing butterfly kisses at each corner. Her stomach muscles contracted in protest.

She felt his fingers on the pearl buttons which fastened the front of her dress. It opened like the petals of a flower and she gasped as he cupped each breast in turn with passionate eagerness.

Her nipples felt fiery, his touch so exquisite that it was almost painful. Hearing her throaty moan of desire, he slid his hand over the curve of her stomach, inside her dress, until his long fingers teased at the waistband of her bikini briefs.

Arching her back in ecstasy, she dropped sooty lashes over her eyes to veil the rising passion she was sure he must read in them. She had said she would never beg for his possession, but it took every ounce of self-control not to do so now.

'Open your eyes, Eden, look at me,' he insisted, his voice thick with desire but very much in command. Like a sleepwalker, she forced them open and found him regarding her with amusement. 'You aren't going to say it, are you?'

Damn him, he had played her like an instrument and she had responded exactly as he knew she would. 'No, I'm not, now or ever,' she snarled, snatching at the gaping front of her dress. 'If this is your idea of coercion, you can wait until hell freezes over before I give in.'

He gave a throaty chuckle. 'Oh, you've already given in, darling. A moment ago, you didn't know the meaning of the word no. A beggar doesn't have to use words to make his needs known.'

'This isn't some kind of power struggle,' she denied, unwilling to admit how close he was to the truth.

'On the contrary, marriage is always a power struggle, and before ours becomes fact I want you to know exactly where the power lies.'

Her face flamed. 'That's the most cynical comment I've ever heard. This isn't about mastery and submission, it's about caring and sharing—two concepts which seem to be foreign to you.'

'It's hardly surprising. There wasn't much of either in my family experience.'

'Your mother told me about your father,' she said, provoking a quick flaring of surprise. 'She also told me how hard you tried to protect her.'

'Hell of a task for a teenager, isn't it?' he said bitterly. 'For all his philandering ways, she loved my father, that was the irony of it. In a way, I think she's still looking for him in the men she marries.'

Such unconditional love was the kind Eden dreamed of finding. Didn't Slade realise how precious Marian's kind of love was in this world? 'They say love is blind,' she said simply.

'Whoever "they" are, they're probably right,' he said on a sigh of frustration. 'I sometimes think I chose my career in communications because my own family did it so badly.'

She had read a magazine biography of him which described how he had worked his way through university by recording staff training cassettes for businesses. His enterprise was so successful that, by the time he had attained his master's degree, he had already laid the foundations for his corporate communications empire.

'At least some good came of your experiences,' she observed, thinking of his meteoric rise in business.

His expression chilled. 'I doubt whether Katie would agree with you.'

'I didn't mean Katie,' she denied. 'What happened to your sister was a tragedy which no one could have foreseen.'

'I tried to talk her out of the marriage, but not hard enough, it seems.'

'You would have done all you could,' she said with unwavering certainty.

'Thanks for your support, however misinformed,' he said in a voice tinged with cynicism. 'You're forgetting that I was the one Julie was coming to when she was killed.'

'And so you think you're responsible for everything else that happened?' Denial vibrated in her tone. 'It isn't true, Slade. Only the greatest conceit would lead you to think it is.'

He gave a wry smile without humour. 'Call it conceit if you like. Face it, Eden, you won't convert me to your starry-eyed views on marriage. I've learned the hard way.'

The gulf between them yawned wider than ever. It seemed as if Katie wasn't the only one who needed to learn the meaning of love. Would she, Eden, have enough strength to teach them both? Or would Slade's bitterness warp her own beliefs in time? She was almost afraid to find out.

She finished tidying her clothes and he held out a hand to her, apparently glad to have this conversation ended. 'Come with me. While Katie's resting, there's someone I want you to meet.'

CHAPTER SIX

THE someone he wanted her to meet was the wedding celebrant, an old friend of Slade's who wouldn't talk to the media or comment on the need for a second wedding ceremony so soon after a first had been reported.

As Eden was coming to expect, Slade's wedding plans went forward smoothly. In the meantime, they had to endure a good deal of teasing comment from the conference participants following Dana's broadcast, but it was well meant. From all but Dana herself, Eden noticed. Several times she caught the journalist watching her, a malevolent expression on her beautiful face.

Well, there was nothing Dana could do to interfere now, Eden thought. She had left with Bob and the other delegates two days before. Reaching behind herself, Eden fastened the long zip of her dress. Her wedding dress, she thought, catching sight of herself in the full-length mirror.

Despite lavish amounts of sun-cream, she had developed a light tan which suited the delicate colour of the dress. The sequins twinkled like stars, and the handkerchief hemline fluttered gracefully around her legs. Even Katie had been impressed by the dress, although she had taken pains to disguise it after her initial gasp of excitement.

'It's very nice,' she had said demurely, but had touched the beaded fabric curiously. 'Mine doesn't have sequins,' she had said almost wistfully.

Without consulting anyone, Eden had ordered a sequinned sash to be made to match Katie's ruffled suit. The little girl's eyes had lit up when she saw it, although her enthusiasm was quickly veiled. 'It probably won't wash, and I'm bound to spill something on it,' she had said primly.

'It will dry-clean,' Eden had assured her. 'By the way, I've made an appointment for you with the hotel hairdresser.'

The little girl had slid her hands under her shoulder-length hair and lifted it experimentally, surveying herself in the mirror. 'Can I have it up?'

'If you want to.'

'Slade says I'm not old enough,' had come the triumphant reply.

Oh, no, you don't, young lady, Eden had resolved there and then. Playing one parent off against the other was the oldest trick in the book and she wasn't letting Katie get away with it. 'Then we'll go and ask him together,' she'd insisted.

To Katie's obvious surprise, Slade had readily agreed to the sophisticated hairdo and Eden had made a score mark in the air. It wasn't much but it was a start.

Now Katie stood at her side, an armful of flowers cradled at her elbow. With her hair swept up in a corona of soft curls, she looked, if anything, younger than her nine years. Eden's heart went out to her. 'Soon you'll officially be my daughter,' she said, her throat closing.

Katie's eyes glistened but she shook her head. 'You'll never be my mummy, and Slade will never be my daddy.'

'Perhaps not, but we can be a family, can't we?'

Katie drew patterns on the carpet with the toe of her black patent shoe. 'A family means you stay together no matter what, doesn't it?'

Wondering where this was leading, Eden nodded. 'I think so.'

'Then you'n me and Slade have to stay together forever, don't we?'

'That's what the wedding vows mean,' Eden agreed.

'Then why did my mummy run away from my daddy and get them both killed?' she demanded, her eyes flooding with tears.

Eden dropped to her knees beside the distraught child. 'Oh, honey, it's terribly complicated. When people get married, they mean to stay together. It's like...like when you pick up something fragile, just to look at it. You don't mean to drop it and break it, do you?'

'Sometimes it's an accident.'

'And that's what it is when a marriage breaks, darling. We do our best to make it work but sometimes our best isn't good enough. Do you understand?'

'I don't know. Maybe.'

'This is a fine time to be talking about breaking a marriage,' Marian said, bustling into the room in time to catch the end of their conversation. 'Come along, you two. Slade is ready with the celebrant and my son can be a devil when he's kept waiting.'

He could be a devil on other occasions, too, but Eden kept the thought to herself. She liked her new mother-in-law too much to burden her with the truth about this marriage.

It wasn't too late to change her mind, came the panicky thought. Once they exchanged vows, she would be bound to Slade in every way. She had meant it when she said she still believed in the sanctity of marriage, so there would be no turning back once she pledged herself to him.

Then she caught sight of Katie preening herself in the mirror. In spite of her determination to be stand-offish, the little girl was already beginning to trust Eden. How could she let her down now?

'Eden, it's time.'

For better or for worse...she was going to marry Slade. Lifting her head, she stepped towards the door, which opened to reveal him looking expectantly her way.

How masculine he looked in a deep blue designer suit, his shirt snowy under the silk tie. Her heart did a back-flip as she caught sight of his brooding eyes fixed on her. It was almost as if... No, don't think beyond the moment, she ordered herself. This wasn't the time to wish for the moon.

The ceremony was a civil one but poetic in its simplicity. For the life of her, Eden couldn't have repeated the words afterwards. Her responses were appropriate and timely, yet she had a sense of unreality about the affair, as if someone else were repeating the vows.

It wasn't until she heard the celebrant say, 'You may kiss your bride now, Slade,' that the dream was replaced with vivid reality.

Cupping her face in warm hands, he lowered his head to hers. 'Congratulations, Mrs Benedict,' he murmured as he claimed his first kiss as her husband.

By Slade's standards it was a chaste kiss but her senses ran riot at the thought of what it symbolised. As his mouth moved over hers, she was achingly conscious that she belonged to him now. Snatches of the ceremony came back. She had pledged him her support in good and bad times, and promised to share everything she possessed with him. Her cheeks burned at the very thought. What on earth had she done?

Her fingers shook as she tossed her bouquet, aiming it strategically towards Katie. Slade had arranged a celebration lunch to be served in a private room of the hotel, then Marian was taking her granddaughter home with her while Slade and Eden enjoyed their honeymoon.

'A honeymoon isn't really necessary, is it?' she had asked when Slade had informed her of his plans.

'Katie and my mother expect it. I thought you'd jump at the chance of a few days' real holiday, after having your break disrupted.'

A holiday with him promised anything but relaxation, she thought frantically. She also disliked being away from her mother for so long, although she doubted whether Peggy would be aware of the time passing.

Since she couldn't share either of her concerns with him, she had been forced to agree.

Now the moment of parting had come and she wasn't nearly ready. This time it was no sham. She was bound to him by marriage with no right to exclude him from any aspect of her life.

'Remember he doesn't have to know *all* your personal secrets,' Marian whispered in her ear as they got ready to leave. 'A little mystery is good for romance.'

She blushed furiously, wishing again that Marian were a little less forthright. Her mother-in-law chuckled. 'The girl can still blush. I hope you realise what a jewel you have here, my son.'

His arm curved possessively around her waist and the hardness of his hip grazed hers. 'I know it, Marian. There's no need to remind me.'

'Then off you go and make beautiful grandchildren.'

With a last hug for Katie, who held herself stiffly but permitted Eden to embrace her, they climbed into the air-conditioned Fairlane Slade had hired for the trip and set off for their honeymoon destination.

Slade had chosen the Blackall Ranges because it was within driving distance of the Sunshine Coast yet well out of any media spotlight.

'Do you know the locals call this the Range of Pleasures?' he asked her as he drove.

'I presume they're referring to the scenic beauty of the countryside,' she returned.

He gave her a wry look. 'What else could they possibly mean? You only have to look around you to see how well named they are.'

Aware of a growing tension inside her, Eden couldn't decide whether he was teasing or not. While they were chaperoned by Marian and Katie, she had felt safe even after they were pronounced man and wife. Now they were finally alone and her nerves were stretched to breaking-point.

She tore her attention away from the man at the wheel and tried to focus on the beauty of the rolling ranges. Once the home of Aboriginal tribes who knew the ranges as Bonyi Bonyi, they were now dotted with cattle farms. The area from Mapleton to Maleny was now famous for its galleries, tea-rooms, boutiques and craft centres.

At this height, well above sea level, Eden was struck by the rich colour of the local flowers. The soil was volcanic, ensuring an abundance of plants and shrubs as well as dense areas of unspoiled rainforest.

Behind them valleys fell away towards the sea and picturesque farms dotted into the distance. It was an idyllic setting for lovers. But not for this travesty of a honeymoon, she thought, closing her eyes against the pain of the idea.

'Tired, Eden?' he asked softly, seeing her lashes droop.

Her eyes flew open. 'No. Well, a little. I thought Katie made a beautiful flower girl, didn't you?'

'Indeed, but never as lovely as the bride.'

The compliment knifed through her, insulting in its blatant hypocrisy. 'There's no need to keep up the act when we're alone.'

His mouth twisted into a wry smile. 'I had noticed. What makes you so sure it's an act? Isn't a man entitled to compliment his wife?'

'It depends on whether or not he means it.'

His hand left the wheel briefly to rest on her knee, the touch so possessive that she recoiled. 'You must know by now that I never say anything I don't mean.'

And he had said he intended their marriage to be a real one, she remembered with a shiver. Suddenly the mountains seemed ominous in their lonely grandeur. 'Have we much further to go?' she asked.

He had returned his hand to the wheel and glanced sideways at her. 'You'd like to keep driving all night, wouldn't you?' Her panicky look confirmed his guess. 'I hate to disappoint you, but we're almost there.'

A short detour off the main highway brought them to a locked gate which Slade operated electronically, admitting them to a park-like property where waterfowl and other feathered creatures wandered along the edge of a man-made lake.

The house itself looked historic with wide timber verandas and cream and green paintwork. It was shaded by ancient camphor laurel trees. Eden was surprised to learn that the house was less than ten years old, having been built jointly by Slade and his sister, Julie, as a family retreat. Now it belonged to Slade alone.

'What are you doing?' she gasped as he swept her up into his arms and carried her towards the house.

'This is our first threshold,' he informed her. Her struggles made no more impact on him than if she hadn't bothered.

'This is ridiculous,' she fumed, as annoyed with the instant flaring of reaction she felt as with his behaviour. It wasn't as if theirs was a real marriage. 'Put me down.'

He didn't comply until they were inside the house, when he set her down on a polished wood floor, in an elegant but comfortably furnished living area. The rustic timber furniture and salmon tonings looked completely at home in the mountain setting. Original Australian etchings decorated the walls.

'Welcome to my secret hideaway, Mrs Benedict,' he said seriously.

Panic flared through her. 'I don't think this is such a good idea.'

He had moved behind a spacious built-in bar and was pouring fruit juice for them both. He had evidently arranged to have the house aired and stocked ready for their arrival. 'Don't you like it?'

'It's beautiful, but it's too...'

'Isolated?' he supplied. 'It's hardly surprising since I've been steadily buying up the surrounding land to keep it that way.'

He put a glass of juice into her unsteady hand. 'It may look rustic, but the property is equipped with the latest security devices, so you're quite safe, I assure you.'

His assurance rang hollow in the face of her real fear. No one had yet invented a security device to restrain an amorous husband.

His eyes met hers, smoky and unreadable, over the rim of his glass. 'You may as well relax. We're here for the next few days.'

How could she relax when she felt so trapped? She must have been mad to agree to this. 'I'd like to look around, if you don't mind,' she said.

'I'll take you for a guided tour.'

She would have preferred to do her exploring alone, away from the determination she saw burning in his eyes. Carrying her across the threshold was only the start, she saw as his eyes followed her every move. He had added a new possession to his empire today and he wouldn't rest until he had put his personal mark on it.

'I'll be fine alone,' she insisted. When he looked at her so intensely, she could feel her control slipping away.

His hand closed around hers and he brought her fingers slowly to his lips, his eyes dark as he regarded her over them. 'You'll never be alone again, Eden. You're my wife now.'

It took an effort to wrench her hand away. 'I don't suppose I'll be allowed to forget it, will I?'

'Not for a minute. But then, I'm assuming once we make it a fact you won't want to.'

'Are you such a dynamite lover, then?'

'There's one way to find out.'

Why did they keep returning to the same subject? Perhaps because the tension which throbbed between them was almost palpable, she realised. She forced a shaky laugh. 'All in good time. How about that tour first?'

'Anything to postpone the inevitable,' he surmised correctly. 'But accept that it *is* a postponement, Eden. Have your tour by all means, but know that it ends in our bedroom tonight.'

With such a caveat, it was hard to concentrate on the house. Her tumultuous thoughts pushed everything else from her mind. Dimly, she was aware of being shown through rooms of different sizes, most with high cedar ceilings and French doors opening on to the veranda.

'Julie had a lot to do with the decorating,' he said, his voice catching a little. His sister had done a magnificent job. The bedrooms were furnished with antiques and lace curtains, and the bathrooms were reproduction in style, done in crisp black and white with coral accessories.

A spacious country-style kitchen was fitted out in pine and granite with every modern appliance. Clearly, no one was meant to slave over a hot stove while staying here. A new wing had been added at the rear of the house. Slade opened a door on to an office complete with computers, a fax machine and walls lined with books. 'This is my domain.'

'It looks like the office back in Hobart,' she observed.

He nodded. 'I can run the company from here if necessary. I come here sometimes when I need to think and plan.'

So this was where he disappeared to when his office was empty for long periods, she thought in surprise. Office gossip had it that he was with his current mistress, but it had seemed unlikely to Eden. He usually returned filled with energy and enthusiasm for a dozen new projects. This was a much more likely explanation.

'Have you seen enough?' he asked, his hand still on the doorknob.

'Yes, thank you.'

'Then you won't mind if I disappear for a short time until dinner? I usually check in with the office once a day in case they need a decision on anything.'

Unreasonably, disappointment gripped her. When he insisted on keeping her company, she wanted time alone. But she didn't want his work taking priority, she thought contrarily. 'I'll manage somehow,' she said airily.

His fingers curled around her wrist as he hauled her close to him. 'You needn't feel neglected. As soon as I tidy up here, you'll have my undivided attention for the rest of the night. This will give you time to prepare yourself.'

If he thought she was going to bathe in scented water and annoint herself with unguents, he was wrong! 'I'll use the time to unpack and write some postcards,' she said flatly.

Mocking laughter danced in his eyes as he gave her a playful push. 'Whatever you do, don't tire yourself out. You'll need all your energy for later.'

Damn him. He must think he was God's gift to womankind, she thought furiously, unwilling to recognise just how aroused she was by his promise. It was exactly what he meant to do, and it infuriated her to find that he had succeeded.

She worked off some of her energy unpacking her clothes and hanging them in the spacious wardrobe, trying not to let her gaze wander too often to the king-sized bed with its fluffy duvet and high pillows.

Sliding cosmetics and brushes into a dressing-table drawer, she froze suddenly. Where was her packet of pills, carefully labelled with the days of the week so she would remember to take them in order? Frantically she searched through her possessions before accepting that she must have left them in the hotel on the coast. With Slade's determination to make their marriage a real one, she couldn't afford to be without them. What was she going to do?

Fortunately she had a spare prescription in her purse. Her eye went to the bedside clock. There was still time to have it filled before the shops closed, and they had passed a chemist's shop on a winding turn just before they left the main road.

Since Slade believed she couldn't have children, he wouldn't understand her urgent need for the pills. She bit her lip. She would have to drive back and get them herself, before he emerged from his study.

The Fairlane was cumbersome to handle along the winding gravel driveway but she took it slowly and was relieved when the electronic gate came into view. The control was on the seat where Slade had left it. She was soon back on the mountain road.

The chemist's shop was further away than she remembered and it took half an hour of careful driving before she reached it. The pharmacist was inclined to chat but she didn't want to be rude in case Slade had regular dealings with the shop. The clock hands crawled agonisingly past as she waited to have her prescription filled.

The chemist handed her the package and her change. 'There you are, love. Staying long in the Ranges?'

'Only a few days.'

'The weather should be kind to you. Whatever you do, don't miss Montford. You can spend a whole day there among the shops and galleries.'

She doubted whether it was what Slade had in mind, but thanked the pharmacist, almost snatching

her purchase off the counter in her haste to be
on her way.

On the way back, the road looked different
somehow and there was a fork she couldn't recall.
Which way had they gone, right or left? Taking the
most likely fork, she found herself at the entrance
to a park.

By the time she reversed back to the main road
and took the other fork, she was almost in tears,
sure that Slade would have missed her by now. It
was much later than she had anticipated.

The door of his study was still closed and she
breathed a sigh of relief as she tiptoed past it
towards the bedroom. Her scream tore the air as a
large figure loomed in the doorway. 'Where the hell
have you been?'

'I... I went out.'

'Without telling me? I've been worried sick about
you. You don't know these mountain roads. You
could have gotten yourself killed.'

His concern sounded so genuine that she had to
remind herself he was only worried about losing a
possession. 'You may be my husband but you aren't
my keeper,' she hurled at him, shaken by the intensity of his anger. 'I don't have to account to you
for my movements.'

His hands gripped her shoulders so hard she
could feel his square-cut nails lancing into her skin.
'Where were you?'

'I told you, I went out.'

'To do what, with whom?'

Sickened by his implacable demands, she threw
caution to the winds. 'I went to meet a man; now
are you satisfied?'

'You little bitch. It didn't take long, did it?'

'What do you mean?'

'For you to show your true colours. We haven't even been married a day before you're making assignations.'

He had taken her at her word, she realised in sick horror. 'Slade, I didn't . . .' she began.

'Did you arrange to meet him again?'

Her head swung from side to side with the vehemence of her denial. 'Slade, there's no one. I only said it because you're suffocating me.'

His eyes were glazed with an intensity which frightened her. He looked like a man pushed to the limits of his self-control. 'Slade?' she probed uncertainly.

His eyes burned into her. 'If you need a man, my dear wife, you don't have to leave this house to find one.'

Dear God, he meant to take her here and now to prove the point. Conflicting thoughts raced through her mind. She wanted him, yes, she couldn't deny it. But not like this, as a demonstration of power.

'Please don't do anything you'll regret later,' she implored.

His hands slid up her back, pressing her hard against him. 'I doubt whether either of us will have cause for regrets.'

Propelled by his hands at her back, she moved into the bedroom. At the sight of the high four-poster, an uncanny sensation took hold of her, its force overwhelming in its intensity. Was *this* sexual desire? If so, it was like a firestorm starting at her core and ripping through every fibre of her being.

He was an incredible man, she thought as he began to strip his clothes off with economical movements. As the trappings of civilisation fell away one by one, she caught her breath at his sheer male beauty. Had she possessed the skill she would have drawn him as he stood before her, every muscle and sinew delineated under sleek, tanned flesh. He was golden all over, except for a tiny triangle at his hips, she thought distractedly. Her eye was drawn to where the dark hair arrowed downwards. She looked quickly away, embarrassed by the hunger in her own gaze.

'Look at me, Eden,' he commanded, catching her under the chin and turning her face back to him.

His eyes held her in thrall as he started to unfasten her dress, dispensing with it skilfully until the garment fell in a foaming mass of fabric at her feet. Her bra followed it, floating downwards in a mist of white lace. Then his hands went to her bikini briefs and shyness gripped her. 'No, Slade, you don't mean this.'

'I've never meant anything so much in my life. I mean to have you, Eden, body and soul. No other man will satisfy you after this, I swear.'

The denial she should have offered froze on her lips as his palms slid down her thighs, carrying her briefs with them, until they joined the pile of clothing on the floor. Seconds later he swept her into his arms and carried her to the vast bed, where he pushed aside the feather covering and placed her on the satin sheet beneath. The coolness sent shivers feathering across her skin, or perhaps it was the passion she saw mirrored in his heavy-lidded gaze.

Desire and fear warred within her. 'I'll hate you for this,' she warned as he rested an arm either side of her, his magnificent body poised above her.

'Then tell me to stop,' he invited, mocking laughter tugging at the corners of his mouth. Without warning, his hand plunged between her legs and she gave a cry of astonishment. His mouth fastened on the roseate peak of one breast, pulling gently at it with his lips until she cried out with the pleasure-pain of the contact. Lifting his head, he turned burning eyes to her. 'Shall I stop now?'

His touch had invaded her most secret places, yet she felt an almost violent hunger for more. 'No, damn you,' she said through clenched teeth.

His fingers trailed lazily across the curve of her stomach until her back arched like a kitten's. 'No, you want me to stop, or no, I shouldn't?'

She could no more have told him to stop than she could have flown, and he knew it. She was his instrument and he played her like a virtuoso, bringing her time and time again to the brink of ecstasy but always withholding the final gratification, until she was dizzy with longing for him. Her hair hung in damp ringlets around her flushed face and she trembled from head to foot. 'Now shall I stop?' he asked, looming over her.

She tried to tell herself that what she was feeling was purely physical. It wasn't love, it was sheer chemistry. Yet all the logic in the world couldn't drive the words from her lips. 'No,' she whispered and this time there was no mistaking the desperate plea in the one-word answer.

When he came to her, the world stopped and there was only the two of them, entwined in the primeval giving and receiving of pleasure. Joy surged through her as she lifted herself to receive the benediction of his love. Her soft cry tore the air, then all was still.

She was hardly aware of sliding into sleep, but was awakened through the night by Slade's wandering touch and seeking mouth. How many times it happened she wasn't sure. She might even have dreamed some of it, for surely no man possessed such superhuman stamina?

It was only as the first rays of sunlight filtered into the room that sanity finally returned. Every muscle ached as she turned her head to look at the man sleeping beside her. Suddenly she was filled with self-loathing. He had made good his promise to possess her but even he hadn't expected her to be such a willing accomplice.

She shuddered at the memory of her abandoned behaviour. He had come to her in anger, determined to prove he was the only man capable of satisfying her. She hated him for it, but she was also very much afraid that he was right.

CHAPTER SEVEN

THE last thing Eden expected from Slade next morning was an apology.

'I never intended to take you in anger,' he said, provoking a wide-eyed reaction. She wasn't sure she wanted him to apologise. It was easier to maintain her rage when he acted like an autocratic beast.

She held herself stiffly, trying to keep a wide swath of the bed between them. Even now, if he touched her again, she wasn't sure she would have the will to resist. 'It wasn't entirely one-sided,' she admitted. Above the pristine sheet, his shoulders were raked with red marks where her nails had found purchase. Dear lord, she had never believed herself capable of such behaviour.

The corners of his mouth tilted upwards. 'I'm well aware that you were a willing participant. In fact, I can seldom remember such enthusiasm.'

She didn't doubt that she wasn't the first woman to share his bed. Nor, probably, would she be the last. His reputation was too well-known. Yet she took no pleasure in his appreciation. There were some talents she wished fervently that she had not demonstrated to him. 'Can we please not talk about it?' she implored, her face hot as she turned away from him.

His hand skimmed her shoulder and down over the creamy mound of her breast. It was the first time she had slept without nightwear in her life, and her skin felt unbearably sensitive. At least, she hoped that was why her skin tingled at his touch. 'Talking wasn't exactly what I had in mind,' he murmured.

She laced her voice with what she hoped was off-putting sarcasm. 'Mornings too, Slade? How will I ever get anything done?'

He gave a throaty laugh. 'Perhaps this will become your main preoccupation. I could think of worse ways to spend our married life.'

She took a deep breath to calm her racing heart. His hand played across her breast near her heart, so he must register the effect he was having on her. Another moment and she would melt into his embrace, as lost as she had been last night. Then, at least, she had had the excuse of provoking him beyond endurance.

Knowing about his father, she shouldn't have mentioned another man, even in jest.

Willing her legs to co-operate, she ducked away from his hand and sat up on the side of the bed. 'I'll have the bathroom first if you don't mind.'

'We could share it.'

'No!' Her fierce denial was a dead giveaway but before he could react she bounded across the room and into the *en-suite* bathroom, where she bolted the door with shaking fingers. His laughter taunted her as the lock scraped home.

At least she was alone for the moment. Trembling with reaction, she managed to work out the complicated tap mechanism and run herself a bath, adding crystals she found in the bathroom cabinet. Moments later, she stretched out in the tub, the carpet of foam closing around her.

Slade might be used to this kind of thing but she certainly wasn't. She ached all over, but he wanted to continue where they left off! More dismaying was the way that the idea set her own senses afire.

Unwillingly, her mind filled with an image of Slade's magnificent body stretched full-length on the vast bed, with only a corner of sheet draped across him. It would be so easy to go back and join him, she thought in disgust. What had he done to her?

Despite her threats, she couldn't accuse him of rape. He had offered her the chance to stop and, heaven help her, she had allowed him to continue. She was as much to blame for what happened as he was. All because of a stupid remark about meeting another man, which had driven Slade over the edge.

'Is there room in there for two?'

Her eyes flew open to find him standing beside the bath. Not even a corner of sheet disguised his male beauty and she blushed furiously. 'I thought I locked the door.'

He pointed to a door which she had assumed led to a cupboard of some kind. 'It's a two-way bathroom.'

Her thoughts were already too errant for her own good. 'You can't come in here,' she denied.

His leg was astride the tub, the foam rising up his firm flanks. 'I'm already in.'

The next thing she knew, he was in the water, bracing himself with a leg on either side of her. Palming a cake of soap, he began to massage the lather into her throat and breasts.

The moment his soap-slick hands touched her skin, her chest tightened, restricting her breathing. 'Don't, please.'

'Very well, is this better?' Deliberately misunderstanding, he moved his soapy hands down her sides, continuing the tantalising motion along her stomach and thighs.

Her body felt leaden, as if his massaging movements had sapped her will. Her head dropped back and her lashes drooped. At the same time, anger warred with pleasure in her mind. What right had he to commandeer her emotions like this? She wasn't a puppet, to be manipulated by the strings he held.

Her head snapped up. 'This wasn't what I agreed to,' she said, as angry with herself as with him this time. 'Have you no scruples?'

His heavy-lidded gaze ignited responsive fires deep within her, but she resisted them. 'What's a scruple?' he asked languidly.

'I might have known the term would be foreign to you. Scruples are those peculiar moral restrictions we put on our behaviour so we don't offend other people.'

He gave a dry laugh. 'A moment ago, you didn't look in the least offended.'

She gathered her wits and pushed his hand away. 'Well, I was. I agreed to marry you to be a mother to Katie, not to be your... your sex slave.'

'Slave,' he murmured, rolling the word around on his tongue as if it was a favourite food. 'While we're discussing definitions—another's property, a chattel, a helpless victim. I doubt if any of those describes you, Eden. Of course, you did have your price.'

'What price?' she asked uneasily.

'My money, my success, a fast track to the things you want from life.'

Her horrified glare raked him. 'Are you suggesting I would sleep with you for those? That would make me no more than a . . . a . . .'

'A wife, Eden,' he said quietly as her mind stalled on a different word. 'Everything I have became yours when we exchanged marriage vows.'

She covered her face with her hands. 'I hate you for suggesting . . . what you just did.'

'I didn't suggest anything. I simply pointed out the facts,' he said coldly. 'You may be confusing hate with something else, my dear wife. Something so close to it that the two are often mistaken for each other.'

'You're wrong,' she said with a shake of her head. She refused to admit that he could know her better than she knew herself. He was the one who was confusing real love with the physical act.

'Time will tell,' he drawled silkily. 'We have until "death us do part", I believe.'

'Must you remind me?'

His fingers gripped the sides of the tub as he levered himself out. 'Apparently I must. You seem to forget that a marriage involves more than the sharing of property.'

Watching him towel himself dry, she swallowed hard. Her intended sarcasm softened into supplication. 'Sex on demand, Slade?'

His eyes gleamed dangerously as he slung a fresh towel over his shoulder. 'Precisely. But this time you'll be doing the demanding, my precious wife.'

'Slade, stop this. Put me down.' Ignoring her shrieks and struggles, he lifted her out of the bath and carried her, dripping, to the next-door bedroom. Her hair was a damp halo around her head and she shivered with coolness and reaction.

Pinning her to the bed with one hand, he began to towel her dry with the other. Her attempts to push him away were pointless. When she snatched the towel, he picked up another and draped it over her stomach, making circular movements which had nothing to do with drying her off.

A furnace began to build inside her, the flames leaping higher and higher with every slow movement. 'Oh, God, please stop,' she entreated, her eyes large as she met his purposeful look.

The towel slid between her legs and he parted them gently to continue drying her. The fire travelled lower, raging deep within her. Without warning, he bent over and claimed her mouth, which was open to protest against his treatment. 'Sweet, so very sweet,' he murmured. 'We must take a bath together more often.'

Twisting her head to one side, she kicked out with her legs, meeting empty air. 'Never,' she vowed. 'I'll have double locks put on all the bathroom doors as soon as we get home.'

His lips traced the outline of her jaw. 'I'll break them down.'

'You can't do this to me.'

'No, Eden?' He feathered her brow with tiny kisses which sent shivers of sensation coursing through her. 'You should have thought of this when you agreed to marry me.'

The towel wound around her felt hot and constricting, the textured fabric teasing her sensitised skin. 'I didn't think it would be like this.'

Stretching out beside her, he flicked the towel aside and grazed his palm across her stomach, smiling at her indrawn breath. 'Lovely, lovely lady. I didn't think it would be like this, either. I sensed the passion in your soul, but I had no idea of its depths.'

'You bastard,' she snarled, trying to grab his hand, anything to stop the exquisite torture of his caresses. She was mortified that he knew precisely the effect he was having. He caught her hand and pressed it to his own body, satisfaction lighting his smoky gaze as he saw her eyes widen. Instinctively, she tried to pull away, but he held her fast until the tactile message of his need for her telegraphed itself to her mind.

'Now you know what you do to me,' he rasped.

What she did to him? Dear lord, what about what he was doing to her? She was on fire, every nerve in her body alert with a desire so powerful that it threatened to dissolve her very being. 'Please, Slade,' she implored, her eyes huge. 'Please?'

Raising himself on one elbow beside her, he began to stroke her, sliding his hand lower and lower. 'Please what?'

'Make love to me.' Her voice was barely audible.

'With pleasure,' he growled, moving over her purposefully. 'And I promise, it will be *with pleasure*, my dear wife.'

*   *   *

How well he had kept his promise. Two weeks later when they returned to Tasmania with Katie, Eden's skin still burned when she remembered her uninhibited responses. It was as if her body had acted independently of her mind. No amount of reminding herself that their marriage was a sham, entered into for mutual convenience, made any difference to his effect on her. It was primitive, mindless, and all-consuming.

In the end, they hardly left the house except to find a new restaurant and assuage a different kind of hunger. If she hadn't insisted on buying gifts for Katie, Ellen and Marian, they would never even have visited Montford at all.

At the famous herb garden they purchased pot pourri for Ellen and herbal cosmetics for Marian. Eden gave a cry of delight over a hand-carved hair ornament which would look lovely in Katie's long hair. Slade looked from the ornament to a range of wooden animals. 'What about these?'

'Aren't they a little young for Katie?'

'Perhaps.' He replaced the toys on the shelf.

She touched his arm. 'I'm sorry, Slade.'

'For what?'

She gestured towards the toys. 'I know you'd like a son to give these things to. Perhaps you made a mistake in marrying me.'

He turned his back on the toy shelf. 'It's hardly fair to blame you for something you can't help.'

His understanding did little to alleviate her feelings of inadequacy. She was surprised to find that she cared about not giving him children. Was the gulf between them narrowing after all?

They had been back at Slade's home in Hobart for less than a week before she was reminded that they were as far apart in their thinking as ever.

'Where are you off to today?' he asked with an annoying hint of indulgence in his tone. He could hardly fail to note that she had come to breakfast dressed in a businesslike linen suit and bow-tied blouse.

Surprise coloured her answer. 'Why, work, of course. I've used up all my holidays.'

Over the coffee he was pouring for her, Slade lifted a sardonic eyebrow. 'It's out of the question, I'm afraid.'

The cup rattled in her hand and she set it down. 'I beg your pardon?'

He calmly buttered a piece of toast as if the woman opposite him weren't about to explode with fury. 'I believe I made myself clear. As my wife, you cannot continue in your old job.'

Her eyes blazed but she took deep, calming breaths. 'Because you say so? It's positively Victorian.'

'Perhaps, but use your head, Eden. How would the other staff react to having the boss's wife breathing down their necks? They'd be convinced you were reporting back to me.'

'But I wouldn't do such a thing.' All the same, doubts registered in her mind. She hadn't considered it from that angle. 'I'm sure I can make them understand.'

He made a dismissive gesture. 'You're the one refusing to understand. The question simply isn't open. You have enough to do here, taking care of Katie and the house.'

'And awaiting your pleasure, you forgot to mention that,' she threw at him, disappointment making her reckless. 'Are you afraid work will make me too tired to do my marital duty afterwards?'

Her anger left him unmoved. 'You do your duty with commendable enthusiasm, my dear. I could be forgiven for thinking you enjoy it.'

'You flatter yourself.' It was humiliating to realise how thoroughly she had betrayed herself on their honeymoon. 'You practically blackmail me into posing as your wife, then give me little option but to make it real for Katie's sake. How can you possibly think I enjoy being left with so little choice?'

He trapped her wrist between long fingers, tracing the pulse-point which betrayed her consternation. 'I think you protest too much. You're forgetting how well I know you now. Besides——' he gestured around the lavishly appointed breakfast-room which looked out on to a patio and pool area '—you lost nothing in the transaction.'

'Nothing but my self-respect,' she retorted, pained that he still thought his wealth had influenced her decision.

Leaning back, he steepled his fingers in front of him. 'Is this job so important to you?'

It was important that she retain some measure of independence against the time when he didn't need her any more. 'Yes, it is,' she said.

'Very well. You can drive to the office with me.'

Elated that she had won a victory, however small, she kept her expression neutral. Inwardly, she was bubbling with excitement. 'Thank you.'

His hooded gaze roved over her. 'I trust you'll still thank me at the end of the day.'

Determined to prove him wrong, she sailed into the office she shared with the other researcher, Denise Garner. Denise looked startled, but bent back to her work after a quick glance at Eden.

'Aren't you going to ask how my holiday went?' Eden queried, sorting through the pile of papers which had accrued during her absence.

Denise gave her a hard look. 'We all heard how the holiday went, Mrs Benedict.'

Stung, Eden bit back the retort which sprang to her lips. 'It's still Eden, Denise. I thought we were friends.'

'A friend wouldn't keep her romance quiet right up till the wedding day.' She gave a bitter smile. 'What an idiot I must have seemed, sounding off about the boss to you when all along you were planning to marry him.'

Eden's heart sank. Without explaining the circumstances, she could hardly correct Denise's impression that she and Slade had been courting secretly for some time. 'It isn't the way it seems,' was the best she could do.

The atmosphere was strained for the rest of the morning. At lunchtime, Denise went out without offering to bring anything back for Eden. Normally, they took it in turns to buy lunch which they ate at their desks. While she was wondering what to do, Eden's phone rang.

'Join me in the boardroom. I've ordered lunch for two.'

Was he deliberately driving a wedge between her and the other staff? 'I can't, it wouldn't be right.'

An impatient sigh hissed into her ear. 'Damn it, Eden. Do you know how hard it is to sit here in my ivory tower, knowing you're a floor below? I must have invented a dozen pretexts to come down, then cancelled them all. The least you can do is have lunch with me.'

Her throat dried, making speech difficult. 'Why would you want to see me?'

'After the week we spent in the Blackall Ranges, you need to ask?'

Her fingers whitened on the receiver. Was *this* why he hadn't wanted her to come back to the office? The chemistry between them radiated down the line. Damn him, why did he have to call now? 'I can't,' she said in a strangled voice and slammed the receiver down.

Barely five minutes later her office door rocked back on its hinges, rattling the windows. Slade came in with a tray balanced across one arm. 'I've brought lunch.'

Over his shoulder, she caught the curious glances of the other staff. 'You shouldn't have. I'm not hungry anyway.'

His eyes gleamed as he set the tray down. 'But I am.' It wasn't for the sandwiches, she soon discovered as he took her in his arms, kicking the door shut behind him.

Everything dissolved into the dizzying warmth of his embrace. 'This isn't right,' she insisted, struggling to surface against the currents of arousal buffeting her.

He flicked small kisses against her eyelids and down her nose. 'It feels fine to me, after restraining myself all morning.'

Ignoring the traitorous stirrings in her own body, she twisted her head to one side. 'Is this all you can think about?'

'With you, yes. And I suspect—correction, I know—you feel exactly the same way, my dear wife.'

Balling her fists, she beat at his broad shoulders, the blows totally ineffective but serving to release some of her tension. 'Your ego won't let you think otherwise, will it?' she demanded furiously. 'Well, you're wrong. I hate what you do to me.'

'It's your own reactions you hate,' he contradicted calmly. 'Why is it so important to you to go on disliking me?'

Because she was sure that their marriage would be over once he knew why she couldn't have children. Didn't she have Joshua's example to remind her of how men reacted to imperfections? As long as she didn't allow herself to care for Slade, she had a defence against him. 'It isn't dislike,' she said, lifting her head, 'it's indifference.'

'Then why did you marry me?'

Her lashes veiled her confused expression. 'You know why.'

He gave a deep sigh. 'For Katie, and the good life I could give you. So why did you insist on coming back to work?'

Too late, she saw the trap in his logic. 'Perhaps it was because you didn't want me to.'

Her stomach churned sickeningly as she waited for him to see through the lie, but he took it at face value. 'So now you have what you want you think you can go your own way, is that it?'

It was what *he* intended to do, she had no doubt. 'Sauce for the goose.' She used her mother's favourite expression.

'By heaven, you try my patience,' he growled, his fingers digging into her shoulders. 'I've a mind to show you that you're playing with fire.'

'Slade, don't.' But his mouth was already on hers, possessive and determined, his tongue probing her soft palate until tendrils of sensation curled through her.

Almost against her will, she found herself responding. Warmth burned along her veins and her hands slid around his neck, her fingers tangling in his hair. It was astonishing how quickly he could drive her to this point.

She was angled backwards against the desk, his body hard and demanding against her, when the office door opened. It was just as quickly pulled shut. 'Oops, sorry.'

'Oh, God, that was Denise.'

Taking his time, he straightened and helped her up, watching in amusement as she tidied her disarrayed clothes. 'It won't help. Your eyes are too bright and your skin is far too flushed to fool anyone.'

Her thudding heart and burning skin confirmed his lazy diagnosis. 'You did it on purpose,' she fumed. 'I'll never be able to work here after this.'

'You could make them understand.' He repeated her words with sarcastic emphasis.

Her withering look moved him not at all. 'You know it won't help. By the end of the day this juicy piece of gossip will be all over the company. And you wonder why I find it so easy to dislike you.'

'You have an odd way of demonstrating dislike,'
he said evenly, but a muscle at his jaw worked,
suggesting that his control was more a veneer than
he wanted. 'I take it I have your official
resignation?'

'From our marriage?' she asked defiantly.

His arms tensed at his sides. 'It would suit you,
wouldn't it? You'd have a hefty property settlement
without fulfilling any of your obligations. Perhaps
you planned this all along.'

Adrenalin coursed through her system as her
body warred with the need to fight him or flee from
him. His suggestion revolted her. 'How could you
think I'd plan such a thing?'

He gave a careless shrug but his eyes glittered
dangerously. 'Women do. I've had plenty of
examples in my life.'

'Well, you're wrong this time. I intend to stand
by my bargain with you.' For as long as he wanted
the marriage to continue, she added silently.
Whatever he thought of her, she wouldn't end this
until he did.

'I should make you prove it to me, here and now.
But I am reasonably civilised,' he added when he
saw her quick flaring of panic. He slashed a hand
through the air. 'Go home, Eden. I can't run a cor-
poration when I'm so distracted.'

Unwilling to believe that she affected him so
strongly, she nevertheless wasted no time in packing
her personal effects and leaving the office.

Her face was scarlet as she ran the gauntlet of
her former workmates. Nothing was said as she left
but the buzz of talk started up as she waited
for the lift.

*   *   *

Making the change from employee to stay-at-home wife and mother was more difficult than she anticipated. Katie was at private school all day and Ellen looked after the house. There was little for Eden to do besides shop and advise on menus.

The one bonus was the freedom to visit her mother more often and she was delighted to see how happy Peggy was at Shepherd House. As her nurse, Fiona, had promised, the quality of care was excellent. Nothing could restore Peggy Lyle to health, but she obviously benefitted from the loving attention which surrounded her.

Eden made the visits while Slade was at work, letting him think she was shopping or at the hairdresser when he called and she was out. He didn't seem to notice anything amiss, and seemed surprised when she confronted him with the news that she needed more to do. 'I thought we'd settled the question of employment,' he said mildly.

'I don't mean a job,' she protested. She was tempted to remind him that he had been the main stumbling-block to remaining in his employ. But she had something else in mind. 'I've been thinking about the house.'

Actually, mansion would be a better word. With its wrought-iron gates, ornate sandstone archways and colonnades, it was an imposing residence, dating back to the late 1870s. The problem was, it had been purchased fully furnished and Slade had changed almost nothing.

'It's comfortable enough,' he said warily.

'Comfortable, perhaps, but not really a home.' The thought had been growing on her for some time.

His mouth tightened into a thin line. 'You were happy enough when we arrived here.'

A lump rose in her throat. It was true that she had hardly noticed her surroundings at first because she was too distracted by his astonishing physical demands. They still made love, but it was different somehow. Almost as if he had tired of her already. She should be pleased that he was more inclined to leave her alone, but, contrarily, she was annoyed.

Her long lashes hid her confusion. 'I'm not complaining about the house, it's magnificent,' she went on. 'But I would like your permission to make some changes, starting with Katie's room.'

Instantly she had his attention. He would pay more heed to a problem with Katie than one with her, she thought on a quick flaring of anguish. 'Is Katie unhappy with her room?'

'She hasn't said anything but it doesn't suit her age group,' she informed him. 'The frills and teddy-bear wallpaper are meant for a nursery.'

He chewed thoughtfully on his full lower lip. She couldn't help recalling the pressure of that mouth on hers, urgently probing and demanding, and she looked away. 'Do as you wish with the room, and the rest of the house,' he said at last. 'Use my charge accounts to purchase whatever you need.'

The subject seemed closed and she suppressed a wave of disappointment. She had hoped that he would participate in the project. It would have been fun to plan and shop as a family. Her eyes closed on the painful awareness that it wasn't what Slade wanted. From the beginning, he had made it clear that playing happy families wasn't his style. So why should she feel so bereft? She didn't want him to act like a real husband, did she? It would mean . . . no, she refused to think she could do anything so foolish as to fall in love with him.

Work provided the best distraction and she threw herself into decorating Katie's room with all the pent-up devotion in her. The little girl was delighted to be consulted on the choice of furnishings and fabrics. Together they spent happy hours after school scouring the shops for the perfect accessories to match Katie's chosen colour scheme.

It was Ellen's day off and a school holiday for Katie so they were making curtains and a duvet cover in matching Laura Ashley fabrics. They were hanging the curtains when the telephone rang. From her perch up a stepladder, Eden said, 'Could you answer it for me, Katie?'

Moments later the child returned looking grave. 'It was someone from Shepherd House. I'm to tell you that your mother is asking for you.'

CHAPTER EIGHT

'I THOUGHT you didn't have any family,' Katie said as they drove to Shepherd House. With Ellen away and Slade at work, Eden had little choice but to take the child with her.

'My mother has been very ill for a long time and I didn't want to worry you,' Eden improvised.

'Oh.' The explanation satisfied Katie for the moment but Eden knew there would be more questions later. For now she welcomed the respite, finding it hard enough to concentrate on driving while she agonised over what could be wrong with her mother. On her last visit, Peggy had been listless but calm enough, although she hadn't talked much.

Please God, let her be all right, Eden prayed silently. If only she had taken the phone call herself instead of sending Katie, she might have learned more. Anxious to get to Shepherd House, she hadn't thought to call back before rushing away.

The nursing home was set high on a hill overlooking the waterfront. As she drove up the circular driveway to Reception, Eden was shaking. She gripped Katie's hand as they went inside.

'I'm so sorry you were worried. It's really good news,' the matron said, alarmed by Eden's white face. 'Peggy is so much brighter today that she insisted we fetch you.'

Eden's legs threatened to give away and tears of relief blurred her vision. 'Oh, God, I thought...'

'Perhaps you'd better use my office to collect yourself before you go in to see her,' the matron advised.

She led Eden and Katie into a sparsely furnished office-cum-sitting-room and pressed a glass of water into Eden's hand. 'I'll leave you alone for a few minutes.'

When the woman left, Eden put the glass down and enveloped Katie in a hug as tears spilled down her cheeks. 'I d-don't know why I'm crying when everything's all right,' she hiccuped.

'Is your mummy going to die?' Katie asked solemnly.

Eden pulled herself together. 'I'm afraid so, darling. When I got the call today, I thought I'd already lost her.'

Katie's finger traced the tears on Eden's cheek. 'You must love her a lot to cry so much.'

'I do. Just as you loved your mummy.'

Katie's eyes brimmed. 'I miss her so much. It's like the worst pain you can ever have inside you.'

Eden held her tightly. 'Oh, darling, I know, and there's nothing anyone can do to take it away for a long, long time. But it does go away at last and leave only the happy memories.'

A kaleidoscope of emotions gripped Eden as she held the frail child in her arms. Maternal love surged through her so powerfully that her heart felt as if it was being squeezed in a vice.

Katie's long lashes feathered her rosebud cheeks and she thrust a finger into her mouth before asking, 'Will you be my mummy, Eden? Then we'd have each other, wouldn't we?'

Wonder flooded through Eden. Out of a shared tragedy might come something precious after all. Katie was finally willing to risk loving again, the first sign that healing was taking place. 'Nothing would make me happier than for you to be my little girl.' Her voice cracked with emotion. 'You don't have to call me Mummy unless you want to.'

Katie gave a decisive nod. 'I want to. Some of the girls in my class have more than two parents, so I can have a second mother.' The decision settled, she went to the window and looked over the waterfront. 'It's raining.'

But not in her heart, Eden thought as emotion threatened to overwhelm her. In Katie she had received a rare gift and no amount of indifference from Slade was going to rob her of it. She blinked away her tears and smiled at the child who had become so important to her. Today she finally felt like a real mother.

They spent the afternoon with Peggy, who was amazingly well. Her speech was halting and slurred, but her memory was sharper than it had been for some time. She took obvious pleasure in Katie's company.

'Your mummy's nice,' Katie confided as they drove home.

Eden blinked hard. 'She loves you too or she wouldn't have asked you to call her Grandma.'

A serious look came over Katie's face. 'I'd better not tell Slade about my new grandma, though.'

Eden had been wondering how to handle this problem. 'Why shouldn't you tell him?'

'If he finds out she's ill, he might think I'm too young to go and visit her any more.'

A sigh of relief escaped Eden's lips. It was a simple, logical, harmless reason and, quite possibly, a valid one. She didn't want Katie to deceive Slade, but it would break her heart to be forbidden to visit her new grandmother. 'It'll be our secret for now,' she promised.

Katie's shy smile illuminated the car. 'Thanks, Mummy.'

The simple word made Eden catch her breath and she shared a radiant smile with her new daughter.

Slade was at home when they arrived. He took it for granted that their absence concerned the redecorating. 'I have a surprise for you,' he told Katie. 'I've arranged for you to come to the television studio with me tomorrow.'

'Wow!' Her eyes shone. It was the first time Slade had suggested an outing of his own accord. 'I'd love it. Wait till I tell my schoolfriends after the holidays.'

'You'll come too,' he said, taking Eden's agreement for granted. 'I know you've sat in on tapings before, so you can explain things to Katie.'

'I'd like that.' It hurt that he didn't welcome her attendance for her own sake, only as Katie's chaperon, but she concealed her feelings. 'Perhaps we could go to lunch somewhere together afterwards,' she proposed.

He frowned. 'I'll be tied up with production meetings all day so I probably won't be free, but you could take Katie out.'

Katie missed the undercurrent of tension between them. 'What sort of programmes are you making?'

'These are educational videos to be used by people in the outback who can't get to a school,' he explained.

It was the series he had discussed with Bob Hamilton at the Queensland conference, Eden recalled. The series which was to star Dana Drury. Was she the reason for Slade's sudden lack of interest in his home life?

'Do you have any animals in them?' Katie persisted.

He ruffled the child's hair. 'Not many, pet. But maybe I can arrange something just for you.'

'That'd be great. Wouldn't it, Mummy?'

At her casual use of the endearment, Slade's eyebrows arched upwards, a curious glint lighting his smoky eyes. He was probably annoyed that they had forged a closer relationship. But what did he expect? Eden refused to keep the child at arm's length, even if it was how Slade preferred his relationships.

'I'm sure it will be fascinating,' she said on a heavy sigh.

Next morning, Katie bounced into Eden's room, unable to contain her excitement about the visit to the television studio. Slade had already left for work but was sending a car for them.

'Slade is going to let me see myself on TV,' Katie enthused. She twisted her hair on top of her head, holding it in place while she studied herself in a mirror. 'Do you think I should have my hair up?'

Eden pretended to think. 'I like it better down but it's up to you.'

Letting the hair drop, Katie looked surprised. 'It is? Then I'll wear it down.'

It was amazing what a little psychology could do, Eden thought. The small victory buoyed her spirits. Maybe the visit to the studio wouldn't be such a trial after all.

She was still trying to convince herself when they were shown into the studio where Slade was working. As part of her job as a researcher with his company, Eden had attended taping sessions before, but this was the first time she was purely an observer. It felt strange to be on the sidelines, trying to keep herself and Katie out of the way.

One person who definitely wasn't on the sidelines was Dana Drury. With her hair and make-up impeccably styled, she looked stunning as she recorded the introductory segment for a tape.

The smile she shared with the camera was sweet and warm. When she finished, Slade walked on to the set and dropped an arm around her shoulder. 'Wonderful, Dana. No wonder you're the darling of the small screen.'

Dana smiled at him. 'It isn't hard to be enthusiastic, darling. This is such a wonderful project.'

Making a face, Katie whispered into Eden's ear, 'Why did she call Slade darling?'

The same question nagged at Eden. 'It's what people in television do. It doesn't mean anything,' she explained to Katie in an undertone.

Inwardly, she wasn't so sure. She and Slade had seen hardly anything of each other since they returned to Tasmania. He had been too busy, working late most nights while she retired to bed, lonely and restless.

The respite should have pleased her but, contrarily, she felt neglected. She had become accustomed to Slade's demands upon her and she missed him. Liar, a traitorous inner voice whispered, you enjoyed his lovemaking. The withdrawal of his attention had left her achingly empty.

But what did she expect? She had known all along that he didn't welcome cloying domesticity. She was supposed to be grateful for the material benefits he had given her in return for becoming a mother to Katie. The last was easy. She had never enjoyed a role so much as she did the unaccustomed one of motherhood.

As for the rest, she was thankful for the freedom from worry which enabled her to look after her mother properly. Slade had kept his part of the bargain and she intended to keep hers by being a model wife. So why did the sight of him with Dana fill her with despair?

'Hello again,' came a sudden interruption.

Startled, she became aware that Len Helliger had joined them. 'Hello yourself. Mr Helliger is a sound recordist,' she explained to Katie.

'And it's Len to both of you,' he chided. 'Are you enjoying your visit, Katie?'

'Yes, thank you, Len. I've never been in a TV studio before.'

'Then come down and I'll give you a ride on my boom microphone,' he suggested with a questioning lift of his eyebrows towards Eden.

Eden gave the little girl a playful push. 'Off you go and enjoy yourself, but do everything Len tells you. OK?'

With a long-suffering sigh which told Eden that her status as mother was now totally accepted, Katie nodded and went off with Len to the brightly lit studio floor.

Moments later, Dana Drury dropped into a chair beside Eden, her heart-shaped face shining from the hot studio lights. Ignoring Eden, she blotted her face delicately and sipped mineral water, while watching the activities on the studio floor.

'It's such a joy working with a professional like Slade,' she said, the sudden admission surprising Eden.

'Have you worked together before?'

Dana's look was almost pitying. 'Not worked, exactly. But we did know each other...ah...very well.'

Which was Eden's cue to ask just how well, she thought. Well, she was darned if she would give Dana the opportunity to needle her with suspicions which were probably groundless. He had married Eden, hadn't he?

Taking another sip of mineral water, Dana laughed lightly. 'You're dying to ask for details, aren't you?'

'Why should I? I didn't ask Slade for a vow of celibacy before we were married.'

'But what about afterwards?'

The question was asked so softly that Eden wondered if she'd heard correctly. The comment made her feel sick at heart but she kept her expression impassive. She said the first thing which came into her head. 'I didn't actually ask for a vow of celibacy afterwards, either.'

Dana's finely pencilled eyebrows arched. 'My, my, such a liberated approach to marriage. No wonder Slade settled on you.'

Eden was driven to ask, 'What do you mean, settled on me?'

'As a suitable candidate for the wife he needed.'

'Because of Bob Hamilton and the money, you mean?'

The other woman shook her head. 'I don't know about the money, but I do know that Slade needed a wife so he could go on seeing me without making headlines all the time.'

Pressure built up at Eden's temples until she felt ready to explode. It was an effort to keep her tone even. 'I'm sure he could have found a simpler way than committing himself to me for life.'

Dana's full mouth twitched. 'For life? What a quaint idea. Given Slade's attitude to marriage, he's hardly likely to agree with you. But I suppose it is convenient to have a babysitter on tap.'

Waves of nausea gripped Eden but she fought them. 'I don't think this is anyone's business but ours.'

Dana's famous smile was cool, all the warmth apparently being reserved for the camera. 'Of course, *ours* includes me.' She put a beautifully manicured hand to her mouth. 'Oh, dear, am I talking out of turn?'

Eden wasn't fooled by the feigned concern. Dana knew what she was saying, and it took considerable will-power on Eden's part to conceal her distress. 'I can't believe we're having this conversation,' she denied. 'It's like a bad script out of a soap opera.'

Dana's husky laugh rippled through the air. 'Where do you think soap operas get their inspiration, if not from real life?'

Eden's mind refused to accept the idea that Dana was involved with Slade, his marriage no more than a smokescreen. 'This is ridiculous,' she said, gaining her feet in a fluid movement.

'Is it? How many times has your husband arrived home early in the last week? Your face tells it all. Not once. And how much energy does he have for you when he is home?' She examined her fingernails critically. 'I hope I haven't exhausted him for you.'

Eden's bleak gaze betrayed the truth—that Slade *had* kept a succession of late nights. When he did come to bed it was to fall into a fatigued sleep.

Dana's explanation wasn't the only possible one but it would explain Slade's recent lack of interest in their relationship.

'Sorry to break up the girl talk, but you're needed on the set, Dana,' Slade said, coming up to join them.

Dana's smile was brilliant. 'Darling, I told Eden that I hope I didn't exhaust you with our late nights last week.'

'I'm sure Eden understands the pressure of work,' he drawled, resting his hands on the back of Dana's chair.

'Yes, she was just telling me what a liberated marriage you two have.'

His eyes glittered and Eden cringed at the way her words were being twisted. 'Was she, indeed?'

Dana gave a provocative laugh. 'She's more honest than most, Slade. Not many women would admit to another woman that they married because of money.'

As she saw his jaw tighten, Eden's mind screamed a protest. 'I was talking about the money you wanted Bob Hamilton to have,' she said.

His cold expression raked her. 'Indeed? What other intimate details did you discuss during your cosy chat?'

He thought she had betrayed his confidence but it was only because she thought Dana already knew about the money. Miserably, she fell silent.

Dana hooked her arm through his. 'We talked about lots of things. You, mostly, since we have you in common.'

The words of denial Eden expected from Slade never came. Instead, he patted the other woman's hand. 'We'd better get back to work.'

Steeling her heart against the ache which wound around it, Eden forced a smile. 'What time shall I expect you for dinner, Slade?'

His backward glance was cool. 'Don't wait for me. I expect to be tied up until late.'

As they walked towards the brightly lit circle, Dana stretched up to speak into his ear and her words carried back to Eden, as doubtless they were intended to do. 'We're at the Australis Hotel tonight, aren't we?'

Eden didn't catch Slade's reply. The nod was enough. A sharp pain cut through her and she slumped, crossing her arms defensively over herself.

It was true, then. Her marriage was nothing more than a smokescreen for Slade's affair with Dana Drury. Perhaps it was planned from the beginning, the bet with Bob Hamilton providing a convenient cover story.

It shouldn't come as a surprise. She'd known all along that Slade wasn't the marrying kind. Nevertheless, she felt as betrayed as a real wife whose husband was having an affair.

'You look like someone who's lost a dollar and found ten cents,' Len Helliger said, coming up to her.

Katie giggled. 'What good would that be? Oh, I see, then you wouldn't look happy, would you?'

For Katie's sake, Eden managed a smile. 'Better?'

'Heaps. Mr Helliger—Len—has invited us to lunch in the comm ... comm ...'

'Commissary,' Len supplied. 'For some reason, canteens in TV studios are called commissaries. It's traditional.'

His light-hearted banter was the balm Eden needed to restore her spirits. She agreed to let Len take them to lunch and accepted his offer of a lift home, since he had finished work early. The meal provided the distraction Eden needed. Little was demanded of her, Katie supplying an endless stream of chatter about her experiences in the studio.

At home, Len refused their invitation to coffee and thrust a videotape into Katie's hands. 'A souvenir of her screen test this morning,' he explained gruffly.

The telephone was ringing as they went inside. Eden picked it up to save Ellen the bother. 'Well, well, if it isn't the surprise bride.'

Recognising the deep voice, she smiled. 'Bob Hamilton, where are you calling from?'

'Hobart, of course. I'm only in town for one day and I hoped you and Slade could join me for dinner.'

'I'm afraid he's working late, but I'll try to reach him at the studio and call you back.'

She noted the number of his hotel room then dialled the television studio, asking to be put through to Slade Benedict in studio four.

There was a long silence then the receptionist said, 'I'm afraid he's already left the building. You can reach him at the Australis Hotel.'

Eden didn't bother writing down the number she was given. She wasn't going to call Slade there or anywhere else. If Dana answered the phone, she would die.

Hanging up, she stared at her image in the hall mirror, hardly recognising her wan reflection. What was going on here? In Katie, and her marriage, she had everything she had a right to expect from life. Why did it matter whether or not Slade was faithful to her?

Unless . . . Oh, God, could she have been stupid enough to fall in love with him? It was the only explanation for the turmoil which racked her. Why else would she care how he spent his nights?

Telling herself it was pure chemistry was no longer enough. The truth had to be faced. She could never have given herself to him with such abandon unless love had begun to flourish between them. No, not between them. On her side, she acknowledged painfully.

He would be horrified if he knew what she was thinking. Love was a minefield he preferred to avoid. Could he have sensed her growing attachment to him before she did, distancing himself before it became a millstone? It seemed all too likely.

Bob Hamilton didn't seem put out when Eden informed him she couldn't reach Slade. 'No problem—you and I will have a good night by ourselves. Serve him right for being a workaholic.'

The word triggered a memory of Dana calling Slade the same thing. Sauce for the goose...but not really, because she had no interest in Bob other than as a friend. All the same, his invitation was an improvement on spending another evening at home alone.

Marriage had certainly improved her wardrobe, she thought as she dressed for dinner. Since Slade believed that she had married him for money, she had bought the clothes in a fit of pique, almost to justify his suspicions. By the time she regretted the impulse as unworthy it was too late. Slade had seen the clothes.

Her choice of a tie-fronted surplice blouse over a straight velvet evening skirt was simple and elegant. It was also vaguely nun-like and she wondered if it was an omen.

Ellen was happy to look after Katie for the evening. 'She'll probably go to bed early after her exciting day,' she said. 'She must have played that videotape of herself a dozen times.' Eden nodded, glad that one of them had gained something from the day.

Bob had made reservations for them in the restaurant belonging to his hotel, a lavish French establishment which might have daunted Eden if she'd been in a less defiant frame of mind.

'Like it?' Bob asked when they were seated.

'It's impressive.'

'But out of a country doctor's budget,' he said. 'Luckily one of my benefactors is paying the bill.'

'A patient?'

'He used to be, when I had a practice in Hobart. Now I work in the outback, he funds my work there and calls on me for a second opinion when he needs one.'

She took him at his word, but she had over-estimated her appetite. When the food arrived she could barely touch it, earning a look of concern from Bob.

'What's wrong, Eden?' he asked, taking the fork from her hand. 'Is it anything to do with Slade?'

'Every marriage has its ups and downs,' she dissembled.

He played with his wine glass. 'So this is a down, right?' When she looked away, he nodded. 'You picked a hard man to tame, I'm afraid. I could have predicted trouble when I first saw you together, even before you were legally married.'

Realising what he'd said, she felt her eyes widen. 'You knew? But how?'

He picked up her right hand and ran his finger along the gold band. 'No wedding-ring, at least not then.'

She grinned. In the rush, neither she nor Slade had thought of a ring until the real ceremony. 'Does Slade know that you guessed the truth?'

He shook his head. 'I hadn't, but your reaction just convinced me I was right.'

'You tricked me.'

'Sometimes it's the best way.'

One thing was puzzling her. 'Why didn't you say anything at the time?'

He twirled the glass in large fingers. 'Slade doesn't need the money from our bet and my kids do. If his pride wouldn't let him be honest...'

She almost choked on a mouthful of wine. '*His* pride? He was worried about *your* pride.'

'I have none where my kids are concerned. I'd beg in the streets if it helped to fund another clinic.'

If only Slade had known, it would have saved her so much heartache. Now the damage was done. 'Men,' she complained. 'You are the most contrary creatures.'

'We need to be, to keep up with our womenfolk,' he said, raising his glass to her in a toast.

Moments later, they were interrupted by the insistent call of Bob's beeper. 'Penalty of dining with a doctor,' he said with an apologetic smile at Eden.

He went to a phone and returned moments later. 'My benefactor and occasional patient is in a bit of bother and he needs my attention.'

'Is it serious?'

He turned grave. 'It could be. His own doctor is out of town so he naturally turned to me. I'm sorry about the evening.'

She waved him away. 'It's all right. I'll take a taxi home. Call me and let me know what happens.'

'You're an angel. I hope it works out for you and Slade.'

Still murmuring apologies, he left and Eden was alone. She didn't feel like drinking coffee without him so she asked the doorman to order a taxi for her. Declining his offer to wait inside, she went out into the cool, refreshing night air.

Seconds later, a sleek maroon Jaguar purred to a stop alongside her and she recognised Slade at the wheel. 'What are you...?' she began.

He gestured impatiently through the open passenger door, his expression grim. 'Get in. I've been looking for you.'

CHAPTER NINE

EDEN barely had time to settle herself on the Jaguar's leather seat before the car leapt away from the kerb. 'Can't you slow down, please?' she asked, snapping her seatbelt into place.

He shot her an angry glance. 'Advice I could well give to you.'

What on earth was the matter with him? 'What's that supposed to mean?'

'Isn't it obvious? Since I wasn't available to take you out tonight, you wasted no time in finding yourself another escort.'

He was angry because he thought she'd been out on a date! It was so preposterous that she almost laughed, thinking that it would serve him right for spending the evening with Dana Drury. It wasn't as if he cared where she was or with whom. He was probably annoyed because she'd taken the initiative. 'How did you know where to find me?' she asked.

'Ellen told me where you'd gone for dinner and Dana told me with whom.'

Her startled glance flew to his face. 'Dana told you? How did she know?'

'She saw you leave the studio with Len Helliger.'

'With Len? I wasn't with Len tonight.'

His hands tightened on the steering-wheel. 'Don't lie, Eden. Dana wasn't the only one who saw you go off in Len's car.'

'Did they also note that Katie was with us? Len dropped us both off at the house then went home to his wife and family,' she emphasised, mortified that he could still suspect her of such behaviour.

'So you arranged to meet him tonight for dinner,' he persisted grimly.

'Why are you doing this? The only person I met tonight was Bob Hamilton, who flew in to see a patient. I only went alone because I couldn't reach you at the studio.'

He sucked in a slow breath. 'I see.'

'What's more, Bob was called to attend his patient halfway through dinner. When he calls you tomorrow, you can accuse him then of having an affair with your wife.'

She was so angry she could hardly see. How dared he accuse her of being unfaithful after spending the evening with Dana Drury? Eden was tempted to demand that he stop the car here and now and let her out.

'I'm sorry,' he said quietly.

Stunned, she released her grip on the door-handle. 'I beg your pardon?'

'I said I'm sorry. When I heard that you'd gone off with Helliger, I saw red. I should have given you the chance to explain.'

'It would have helped,' she agreed, her temper cooling a little. Knowing about Slade's father, she shouldn't be surprised if he reacted so badly over her dinner with Bob. All the same, she couldn't help wondering why he should care so much, when he plainly didn't love her.

He spun the car around a sharp turn and the seatbelt cut into her breasts. She looked around, confused. 'This isn't the way home.'

He shook his head. 'We're going to Dana's apartment. She telephoned to say that she needs me.'

If he had punched her, she couldn't have felt more shocked. After calling her to account for an innocent evening out, he was openly flaunting his interest in Dana. 'Wasn't it enough that you spent the evening with her?' she asked, unable to keep the bitterness out of her tone.

His fingers drummed a tattoo on the steering-wheel. 'We worked late this evening, which is hardly the same thing. The Australis Hotel lent us their facilities for one of the videos. The studio should have told you where I was when you called.'

A confusing morass of emotions threatened to engulf her. Had he really been working at the hotel with Dana? Was their so-called affair merely a product of her suspicious mind?

'Did Dana tell you what her problem is?' she asked.

Lights from an oncoming car flared through the Jaguar, illuminating Slade's world-weary expression. Then the interior darkened and his voice reached her out of the shadows. 'You may as well know what's going on. Dana wanted something to happen between us tonight and when I wouldn't co-operate she became depressed.'

'But she has so much.' Why did she want Eden's husband? was the unspoken corollary.

'Not as much as everyone thinks. Her career is teetering on a knife-edge. The ratings have slipped lately and the channel is thinking of bringing in a co-presenter to revitalise things.'

Eden began to understand a little of the other woman's dilemma. 'She's never shared the limelight with anyone.'

He nodded, his profile finely chiselled in the flickering street-lights. 'I doubt if she knows how. She's been written up as Superwoman for so long that it's a struggle to live up to her own image.'

A shiver shook Eden. 'I'm glad I'm not a public figure, having to live up to everyone's expectations.'

'Nobody forced Dana to become Superwoman. She wanted it and now she's paying the price.' There was a chill in his voice which suggested there was more.

Her head jerked up, fright widening her eyes. 'Do you think she could be suicidal?'

'She's made threats and they're never to be taken lightly, even in jest. When I wouldn't stay with her after we wrapped it up tonight, she dropped hints about what she might do. I didn't take it seriously until she called me at home, very drunk, demanding to see me. I want you with me when I do.'

'You don't think she'll actually do anything, do you?' she asked shakily.

'Perhaps not. But I can't ignore her call just in case.'

It was one of the oldest ploys to bring a man to heel, Eden couldn't help thinking. For now it seemed to be working. But what would Dana do when Slade turned up with her, Eden, in tow?

Her heart was pounding as they parked outside an exclusive high-rise apartment block in one of the best parts of Hobart. At Slade's suggestion,

Eden stayed out of range of the security cameras while he identified himself.

Through the intercom, Dana's voice sounded slurred. It took several attempts before she got the security doors open and they were able to go inside. A luxuriously appointed lift carried them to her apartment, which occupied the entire penthouse floor.

Her front door was open and she lounged in the doorway wearing a grey silk nightdress and négligé, her dainty feet bare. 'Darling, you came!' she exclaimed as Slade stepped out of the lift. Catching sight of Eden behind him, she made a face. 'Why did you have to bring *her*?'

He took a grip on Eden's arm and propelled her with him into the apartment. Dana went to a pearl-blue granite bar and mixed herself a drink. Eden looked around, seeking clues to this complex woman.

There was none in the apartment, which was designed for show rather than comfort. A wall of tinted glass opened on to a vast terracotta-tiled terrace with a spectacular view of the city beyond. Downlights, recessed into raked ceilings, gleamed like stars overhead, firing pin-points of light off the predominantly chrome and glass furnishings.

There were no signs of a private life. No photographs or mementoes, only carefully arranged *objets d'art*. Eden shuddered. She had thought Slade's mansion at Nutgrove Beach lacked warmth, but this was positively arctic.

'You said you needed me, Dana.' Slade's ringing tones jolted her to attention.

Dana gestured with her glass, which looked to contain neat whisky, and not her first by any means. 'I said I needed you, not a *ménage à trois*.'

His protective arm was warm around Eden's shoulders as he drew her closer. 'Eden is my wife. You may as well accept the situation.'

Downing half of her drink, she laughed. 'Dana Drury doesn't have to accept anything. You don't love her. You only married her as a cover so the media would leave us alone.'

At Eden's shocked intake of breath, his hold tightened reassuringly. 'You don't know the first thing about it. I married Eden because I love her, not for any other reason.'

Knowing it was said to convince Dana didn't prevent a bright flame of desire from leaping inside Eden. What if it had been true instead of a convenient fiction?

The other woman's face was a twisted mask of hatred. 'I don't believe it.' She splashed more whisky into her glass, spilling some across the granite surface. A generous amount made it into the glass and she drank it in one swallow. 'You can't love her. I can't lose you, too.' The last word came out as a desperate whisper.

'You haven't lost anything except a little pride,' Slade reasoned. 'It will still be your show.'

'You don't understand. It's the only love I have. I can't share it, I can't.'

Eden's heart went out to the woman. How could she have envied such a brittle shell whose only emotional succour came from an unseen audience? No wonder she couldn't face the prospect of sharing it.

Unexpectedly, Slade swung towards the window, resting his hand with apparent casualness on a glass and chrome *étagère*. 'She has so much, doesn't she, Eden? This fabulous view, for one thing. Have you looked at it?'

How could he admire the view when Dana was destroying herself before their eyes? 'I don't think . . .' she began.

His cutting gesture throttled off her objection. 'Come and see the view, now,' he insisted.

The steely edge in his voice moved her to obey. Standing where he ordered, she saw what had captured his attention, and it wasn't the spectacular outlook. On the *étagère* stood a bottle of livid capsules. The label identified them as sleeping-pills.

With a deft movement Slade slid the bottle into her hand. 'The doctor's name and number are on the label. Find a phone and call him,' he murmured into her ear.

She nodded, stepping away from him and pocketing the bottle. 'Could I use your bathroom?' she asked Dana.

Dana made a vague gesture towards a corridor off the main room. 'S'in there. Take your time.'

She probably welcomed the excuse to be alone with Slade and try to talk him round. But the threat no longer troubled Eden, who was too intent on trying to locate a telephone. She found one in the master bedroom and sank on to a vast, fur-covered bed to make the call.

The doctor was out but a redirection service tracked him to a private party and in minutes she was speaking to him. He heard her out and promised to come over straight away. With a sigh of relief, she hung up and found her way back to the living-room.

Dana was stretched out on a leather couch, her mascara-smudged eyes closed. 'She passed out,' Slade said.

Eden handed the pills back to him. 'Maybe it's for the best. Her doctor's on his way. Luckily he wasn't far away.'

Slade weighed the almost full bottle in his hand. 'It's just as well I took her call seriously. If she'd taken these on top of the alcohol, she might never have woken up.'

'You saved her life,' Eden said, pride glowing in her voice.

He shook his head. 'We did it together.'

She brushed damp strands of hair off her forehead. 'I wondered what had gotten into you when you asked me to look at the view.'

He gave a heavy sigh. 'When will you learn to trust me?'

Her glance went to the sleeping woman then to the strong man standing over her like a sentinel. 'Maybe I had my first real lesson tonight.'

'You didn't believe all that nonsense about our marriage being a front for my affair with Dana, did you?' His eyes darkened and he frowned. 'You *did* believe it. Why the hell didn't you say something instead of letting the suspicion fester?'

She looked away. 'I think I was afraid of the answer you might give me.'

'Good God, woman. Have you learned nothing about me since we got married?'

He crossed the room and took her in his arms, shaking her slightly to emphasise his point. The gesture lifted her momentarily off her feet, pressing her hard against him. She suppressed a groan of desire, wanting him as she had never done before. How could she have doubted him?

Yet there was his indifference since they arrived home. It was a long time since they had made love, when he had been so demanding at the beginning. If there was no one else, why didn't he want her any more?

She was about to ask when the intercom buzzed, announcing the doctor's arrival. Slade admitted him and explained the situation, then stood back while he examined his patient.

'You were wise to call me. I'll take care of her from here,' he assured them. He offered to stay with Dana until an ambulance arrived and she could be taken to a private clinic where her depression could be treated.

'You're sure she'll be all right?' Eden asked anxiously. She bore the other woman surprisingly little ill will. In many ways, Eden understood her desperation. It must be dreadful to be loved by everyone and no one.

Slade took her arm. 'We've done all we can here. It's time to go home.'

Home. What a haven it seemed after the night's events. The sound of the great wrought-iron gates swinging shut behind the Jaguar was music to her tired ears. Emotionally, she was a wreck. It was no time to be making decisions which could affect the rest of your life, but she knew she was about to make one all the same.

In the harrowing aftermath of Dana's experience, she was being forced to face a truth she had been avoiding for too long. She was in love with Slade Benedict.

It was rash and probably fatal. He didn't love her and he didn't believe in the kind of marriage she wanted above all. Yet, against all the odds, she had fallen in love with this arrogant, demanding, insatiable man. Agreeing to marry him for mutual convenience, she had fooled no one except herself.

She choked back a sob. She could imagine how he would react to a declaration of love. He had handled Dana's unwanted affection adroitly enough. Doubtless, he had ways of dealing with a lovesick wife as well.

He parked the car and stretched his arms, his fingers loose around the steering-wheel. 'God, what a night. I could fall asleep right here.'

She began to hum a few bars of 'Wake Up, Little Susie' and he laughed, a warm, chocolate sound which sent goose-bumps up her spine. 'Point taken. If we fell asleep here, we would be in hot water, not only with Ellen, but with our daughter. However would we explain it?'

'It would be difficult,' she agreed. 'I'm exhausted, too, but I couldn't sleep just yet.'

'Join me for a nightcap,' he suggested.

It was playing with fire. With her new-found awareness, it was probably wiser to go straight to bed, but it was almost dawn and she felt most unwise. 'All right.'

'I'll make it while you change.'

Refusing to examine her motives too closely, she took a quick shower then dressed in a lacy tricot lounging suit of softly draping top with a side-tie over pull-on trousers. In a mist of Joy perfume, she floated down to the living-room where Slade had their drinks ready.

He sniffed the air appreciatively. 'You smell wonderful.' His lips grazed the side of her neck as he handed her a drink in an ice-frosted glass.

His nearness forced her to place a steadying hand on his chest. He had cast aside his tie and unbuttoned his business shirt to the waist. His chest hairs rustled against her palm. A low moan began in her throat and she clamped her lips shut. This was definitely a mistake.

His eyes gleamed brightly, the gold in the grey-green depths hypnotising her, making it impossible to move away. 'It was quite a night, wasn't it?' she said, casting around for something, anything, to say to defuse the tension which arced between them like electricity.

'Quite a night,' he echoed, his lips close to her cheek.

'Do you think Dana would really have done something reckless?' she asked, her voice a hoarse whisper which sounded loud in the dark, sleeping household.

A smile tilted up the corners of his mouth. 'I don't know, but I think I might.'

'What do you——?' The words were crushed by the sudden invasion of his kiss. He took the drink from her and set it down on a side-table, then drew her irresistibly into his arms.

There was something different in his touch this time, something infinitely more tender. It was no less demanding, but he seemed more ready to give than to take from her.

Inside his shirt, her hand spanned his ribcage, noting the rise and fall of each breath. It was like the ebb and flow of the tide, and his heartbeat, strong and virile, provided a counterpoint. With a sweeping movement, he hooked a hand under her knees and lifted her, placing her on to a shaggy wool rug in front of the fireplace. The long hairs teased her skin, making it unbearably sensitive. His touch felt so electric that she half expected sparks to fly with each caress. He was kneeling beside her, his arm cradling her back while he kissed her forehead, nose, cheeks, throat and, sweetest of all, the swelling curve of her breasts. Releasing the tie of her top, he let it fall away and kissed the roseate peaks in turn until she stifled cries of ecstasy deep in her throat.

Alarm bells rang inside her. Loving him made it all the harder to accept his seduction. She wanted him to care. Only then would his lovemaking be truly meaningful.

She should push him away. So why did her fingers tangle in the thick waves of his hair, the shorter hairs at the nape furring against the pads of her fingers? She had never noticed before what a variety of textures his hair yielded. The discovery silenced the inner voices of caution and she began to explore every inch of him, the soft and the hard, the rough and the smooth.

'Have you any idea what you're doing to me, woman?' he demanded on a sharply indrawn breath.

'I'm exploring,' she said over the siren call of her conscience. Knowing that she loved him, it seemed important to investigate every part of him. One day these memories would be all she had. 'I feel I hardly know you,' she observed.

'Are we talking in the clinical or the biblical sense?' he drawled.

She closed her eyes, hardly able to force the words out. 'Perhaps both.'

He gave a throaty chuckle. 'I think we know one another very well in the biblical sense. Maybe it's time for the other.'

Before she could summon a protest, he slid her lounging pyjamas down her legs, a cool breeze invading her skin. A shiver had hardly begun when the warmth of his caress supplanted it. With each sweeping stroke, she arched her back, her soft mewing pleas urging him on. When he bent his head to allow his mouth to follow the trail blazed by his hands, she could hardly bear it. He was making good his promise to know every part of her and the sweet invasion threatened her sanity. Her mind screamed for him to stop, while her responses urged him on. She wanted him. She needed him. She loved him. He was wholly hers for this moment, no matter what the future held.

There was a moment when even Slade's iron control reached its limit. His chest rose and fell in savage rhythm as his knee gently sought the junction of her thighs. As if in slow motion, she arched under him, welcoming the fiery touch as he came to her at last.

He surrounded her, filled her, fired her with such a tumult of sensations that her very reason was in jeopardy. Silken tissue met rigid flesh in what began as a demonstration of his mastery but became a quest for unity. She fused, melted, bonded with him until she could no longer tell where she ended and he began.

Now, now, her mind repeated over and over. Nothing else mattered but the blinding, all-consuming need to be loved by him.

'Oh, Slade, Slade.' His name was the only sensible word her whirling brain could summon.

Above her, his lips found hers. 'I know, my darling. I didn't mean this to happen but you're a fever in my blood.'

What did he mean? Didn't he want to make love to her? The thought that it might already be over between them drove her to demonstrate what she couldn't put into words. He sensed the change in her, responding to it in ways which took her breath away. It was torture of the sweetest, most tantalising kind. Tremors rippled through her, building in intensity until she clung to him as if to a lifeline, her slight body racked by wave after wave of exquisite torment.

Minutes or hours later, she lay exhausted in his arms, the rug soft beneath her. 'We should go to bed. What if Katie comes in and finds us like this?'

He levered himself up on one elbow. 'Nine is plenty old enough to start learning about the birds and the bees. If she were younger, we might have a problem.'

He paused thoughtfully. 'Are you positive that children are out of the question, Eden?'

Tension replaced some of her languor. 'What makes you ask me now?'

'You're an ideal mother. Perhaps we should consult more doctors, make sure you've had the best advice.'

'It won't change anything,' she said on a sigh. So he was still dreaming of the son she dared not give him. Anxious to change the subject, she said, 'We'd better get up before you have some explaining to do to Katie.'

Her ploy worked. 'Since when is it my job? Mothers are supposed to teach their daughters about such matters.'

'Which is probably the only reason you married me,' she retorted, fearing it was close to the truth.

He kissed her ear, his tongue curling teasingly into the orifice. 'There may be other reasons.'

Resisting the temptation to press him, she scrambled to her feet and gathered up her scattered clothes. More than anything she wanted to hear that his reasons included love, but her throat closed on the question. What if he gave the wrong answer? She wasn't sure she could stand it tonight. 'I'm going to bed,' she said. 'Are you coming?'

His languid look glided over her slim contours, outlined in lamplight. 'You go. If I come with you now, we may not get any sleep at all.'

So it was still purely physical on his part, she thought as she made her way through the darkened house to their bedroom. Even at the height of their passion, he had breathed not a word of love to her, although her heart had been bursting with love for him.

Face it, he isn't going to say what he doesn't feel, she chided herself. All the love was on her side and her naïve attempt to seduce him with perfume and provocative clothing had achieved its aim, but not a whit more. He hadn't wanted to make love to her until she fanned the flames of his desire. She had practically thrown herself at him, and her cheeks flamed with self-mortification.

They couldn't go on as they were. She sat bolt upright in bed, the thought strong in her mind. As things were, she wasn't a wife in any sense beyond the physical. She had thought it was enough but it was tearing her apart. She had to know if he could ever love her. And that meant being honest with him about her family's medical history.

A sob burst from her throat as she imagined his reaction. Would he turn away from her in disgust, as Joshua had done? Or would he suggest that it was better if they went their separate ways?

The scenes played over and over in her mind until she fell into a troubled sleep, her dreams filled with Slade. He was invariably walking away.

It was a shock to find him standing at her bedside next morning, like a ghost from her disturbed dreams. His expression was unrelenting.

'What is it? What's the matter?' she asked, sitting up. Had she imagined her languid lover of last night? This morning, he looked like an avenging angel.

'This is what's wrong,' he said, holding out a strip of foil dotted with coloured tablets. 'I take it these are yours?'

'Yes, they're mine,' she admitted tiredly. Why did he have to find them now, before she could tell him in her own way?

'You lied when you said you couldn't have children, didn't you?'

'It isn't a lie. I can have them physically, but I mustn't.' She buried her face in her hands. 'How can I make you understand?'

He tossed the pills on to the bed beside her. 'I understand all right. This explains why you're never at home when I call, yet you never have any purchases or a new hairstyle to account for your time. You never had any intention of being faithful, did you?'

'You're wrong, so wrong.' Her breath came in heaving sobs as she fought to get the words out to make him understand. But it was too late; he had already slammed out of the bedroom.

CHAPTER TEN

'SLADE, wait.' Frantically, Eden pulled on a kimono and raced after him, catching up with him in the living-room. His face was set in stone and his body language spoke total rejection. She wasn't sure he even heard her.

'I was going to tell you today,' she volunteered.

He swung around, his eyes blazing. 'Tell me what? More half-truths? I thought we'd reached a point where we could be honest with each other. Now I find you're up to your old tricks, twisting the truth to suit yourself.'

'You're never going to let me forget about that job application, are you?'

'I'd already forgotten it, until I was forcibly reminded while searching for some sunscreen lotion for Katie this morning.' He spread his hands wide. 'No wonder you were ready to suspect me of having an affair with Dana. It takes one to know one, doesn't it?'

With no defence against this accusation, she turned away. It hadn't occurred to him to wonder why she cared if he was having an affair. She wished that she had trusted him enough to ask outright, but it was too late now. The damage was done. He wouldn't believe anything she told him after this.

'It seems we're at an impasse,' she said dully. 'Do you want me to go away?'

169

'No!' The strangled cry followed by the door slamming drew their attention. Eden's shocked look went to Slade. 'How much do you think Katie heard?'

'More than enough.' Wrenching the door open, he led the way into the corridor but there was no sign of the child. 'She can't be far. You check the house, I'll look in the grounds,' he instructed crisply.

Eden took the stairs two at a time but Katie's room was empty, the lace curtains billowing at the open window. She went to it and looked out, spotting Slade below. He was also alone.

'Have you seen Katie?' she asked Ellen in the kitchen.

The housekeeper was rolling out pastry and gestured with floury hands. 'She ran through here as if the devil were on her heels. I asked her what was the matter, but she didn't stop.'

Eden's heart sank. 'She overheard Slade and me having an argument. I think it reminded her of her parents.'

Ellen wiped her hands on a tea-towel. 'Poor child. I'll come and help you look. She needs to know that every argument doesn't mean the world is coming to an end.'

It would be hard to explain this one away, Eden thought, as doubt assailed her. If the little girl had heard Eden mention leaving, the results could be disastrous. They had to find her.

A thorough search of the house and grounds revealed no sign of Katie. Then Slade reported finding a hole in the bushes alongside the electronic gates.

'It's just big enough for a child to squeeze through,' he told them.

'If she's left the grounds, where would she go?'

They tried calling the school, which was closed for the holidays, but a caretaker answered and promised to look out for a distraught child. Calls to several of Katie's friends were equally unhelpful.

'I have something,' Ellen reported. 'I found this on the hall table where we usually put the mail.'

It was a hastily scribbled note. The childish writing said, 'Gone to Grandma's.'

Slade reached for the telephone. 'I'll alert Marian and the airport in case she makes it to the Gold Coast. God knows, she's ingenious enough to find a way.'

He began to dial but Eden's fingers closed on the telephone, cutting him off. 'She isn't headed for Queensland,' she told him, her heart hammering painfully. 'I think I know where to find her.'

With shaking hands, she dialled Shepherd House and asked for the matron. Slade watched, anger surrounding him like an aura. She could tell he thought this was another example of her deviousness. No matter what the consequences to herself, she prayed that her hunch was correct.

When the matron answered, she described Katie and asked whether anyone had seen the child. When the answer came, relief made her slump against the wall. 'She's safe at Shepherd House,' she said, feeling her eyes fill with tears.

His lip curled into a sneer. 'Since you have all the answers, I suggest you give me directions. I'll drive.'

As they drove, he gripped the wheel with savage intensity, taking risks with the traffic which she had never seen him do before. He was normally a fast but careful driver. 'There's no need to get us both killed to get even with me,' she said as he cut in on another car.

'Getting you killed would be a kindness compared to what I'd like to do to you,' he growled and she shivered. 'This time you've gone too far, involving an innocent child in your schemes.'

She flinched as if from a blow. But this wasn't the time to worry about herself. Until they had Katie back safely, nothing else mattered. 'Turn here,' she instructed belatedly, gripping the door-handle as the car screamed round the corner on two wheels.

'What is this, some kind of school?' he demanded as they pulled up outside the nineteeth-century seminary which was now Shepherd House.

'It's a hospice for people with degenerative illnesses,' she explained in a tired monotone.

Before he could quiz her further she hurried up the steps. The matron was waiting for them in the reception area.

'I thought it was odd when the child turned up here in a taxi on her own. If you hadn't telephoned, I was going to call you.'

'Where is she?' Slade demanded impatiently.

The matron directed her answer to Eden, unimpressed by Slade's abruptness. 'She's in the television-room with your mother.'

Eden knew the way. As they hurried along the corridor, Slade's grip on her arm was punishing. 'Your mother? This gets better and better.'

The tension inside him was palpable. He was like a coiled spring. When the force was unleashed she knew who would be on the receiving end. The prospect was daunting, but she would deal with it when the time came. For now, all her concern was for Katie.

There were only two people in the television-room. Peggy Lyle sat serenely in a wing-backed chair, her pale face almost empty of expression. She hardly seemed to be present at all, except in a physical sense. Katie didn't seem to notice as she chattered to Peggy and worked the television set by remote control. They were watching the videotape Katie had made at the television studio the previous day.

'This is called a screen test, when they try you out to see if you're any good on television,' Katie explained to Peggy.

Belatedly, the child noticed Slade and Eden in the doorway. 'Oh, it's you.'

'We were worried about you, sweetheart,' Eden said softly.

'You weren't worried about me when you planned to go away.'

Eden went down on her knees and took the child in her arms. She was stiff with hostility. 'Don't you know how much we love you, Katie?'

'My mummy loved me too,' she said stubbornly. 'It didn't stop bad things from happening.'

'I know, and I'm sorry if you thought it was going to happen again because you heard Slade and me arguing.'

Katie's chin jutted out. 'You and Slade were yelling at each other, just like mummy and daddy did before . . .'

'So you ran away before anything bad could happen.'

Katie looked up at Slade apprehensively. 'I didn't really run away. I took my pocket money and came to visit Grandma. She said I could come any time.'

Peggy Lyle reached out awkwardly and tousled the child's hair. 'You're a good girl, just like your mummy.'

The words were so slurred as to be barely understandable but Katie translated for Slade's benefit. 'Grandma thinks Eden's my real mummy.'

'So I gather. You can tell me all about it at home, Katie. It's time to go now.'

The child's uncertain glance went to Eden. 'Are you coming home too?'

'Of course, sweetheart.'

'Then you and Slade aren't going to fight any more?'

A sharp pain lanced through Eden. 'I can't promise, darling. Could you promise never to get angry about anything ever again?'

Katie thought for a moment. 'I suppose not.'

'Then neither can grown-ups. But we *can* try.' She prayed that Slade wouldn't contradict her, at least until they were alone. For the moment, Katie needed every bit of reassurance they could offer.

She drew Slade forward and placed his hand in Peggy's. 'Mother, I want you to meet my husband, Slade Benedict.'

'Pleased to meet you, Mrs Lyle,' he said gently, studying the frail woman in front of him. How

Eden wished he could have met Peggy when she was well, full of laughter and vitality. They would have got on well, she felt sure.

There was only the faintest spark of response as Peggy looked at Slade. 'Hello.'

'She doesn't say much to strangers. Talking is hard for her,' Eden explained.

Peggy brightened noticeably when Katie came forward for a hug. Slade took a step back. 'They don't seem to have any communication problems,' he observed wryly, watching Katie and Peggy together.

'She seems to sense that Katie accepts her as she is. Adults rarely offer that kind of acceptance.'

He raised an ironic eyebrow. 'Trying to tell me something, Eden?'

What was the point when he had already made up his mind about her? She took the child's hand as they started for the door. 'Aren't you taking your videotape?' she remembered.

Katie shook her head. 'I'll see it when I visit Grandma again. I thought she'd like it to keep her company.'

A lump rose in Eden's throat. 'I'm sure she'll enjoy it,' she managed with difficulty.

Slade's silent condemnation hung over her like a cloud as they travelled home. She almost would have preferred him to berate her. Anything was better than enduring his cold rejection. She knew he was containing himself for Katie's sake and was foolishly grateful, although the time wasn't far off when she would bear the full brunt of his pent-up fury.

Ellen treated the little girl like a prodigal daughter and immediately volunteered to take her out for the day. They were discussing where they would go to have lunch when the door closed behind them.

Eden waited until she heard Ellen's car drive away before she looked at Slade, unconsciously squaring her shoulders. 'There doesn't seem to be any harm done, thank goodness.'

'It depends whom you're referring to,' he said coolly. 'Katie hasn't suffered, I'll grant you. But it seems you have a whole secret life you haven't deigned to share with me.'

The heavy sarcasm in his voice wounded her but she faced him unflinchingly. 'The kind of marriage you wanted didn't seem to require an exchange of confidences.'

If Slade had been angry before, it was nothing compared to the murderous rage she provoked in him now. His white face and searing gaze made her take a step backwards. 'Don't worry, I won't hit you,' he ground out, 'although, God. knows, I probably should. But I still have some standards left, even if you don't.'

'That's unfair,' she denied. 'All I did was——'

He silenced her with a slashing gesture. 'All you did was mislead me from the moment I set eyes on you. Damn you, why did you tell me you had no family?'

'I didn't tell you. I left a blank when I applied for a job with your firm.'

'You left more than a blank,' he railed. 'You deliberately let me think you had no one, even after you agreed to marry me.'

Her defences crumbled in the face of his relentless anger. She felt as if a great storm was buffeting her, threatening to knock her off her feet, and she gripped the back of a chair. 'I don't deny it, but I had good reason.'

He swore under his breath. 'I'll bet you did. Well, I'm waiting, but try and make it the truth this time, if you still recall what the word means.'

She swayed, feeling physically battered by his attack. 'Oh, I know what the truth means,' she said grimly. 'I had to face plenty of it when I was told what was wrong with my mother. She has a genetic illness which only shows itself in middle age. I didn't tell you because...'

'Because it's the kind which skips a generation, and can be passed on to any children you may have,' he interpreted with devastating accuracy.

'So now you know why I mustn't think of having children of my own,' she said stiffly, fighting to keep from breaking down completely. Where were the words of reassurance, of love, which she longed to hear? Why didn't he tell her that it was all right, none of it mattered to him as long as they were together?

She almost laughed aloud at her own thoughts. Surely she had enough experience by now to know that what she wanted was impossible?

He raked a hand through his hair. 'God, Eden, why didn't you trust me enough to share this with me?'

She gave a hollow laugh. 'The last man I told couldn't get out of my life quickly enough.'

'It's a lot to come to grips with.'

She might have known he would sympathise with the man who walked out on her. 'You should try being in my shoes.'

His answering look was bleak. 'How long did you plan to keep it a secret?'

'With the kind of marriage we agreed to, it didn't seem to matter, as long as I was a good mother to Katie.'

A look of utter weariness darkened his features. 'So it was all for Katie, was it?'

It was for you, too. The words rose in her throat but she throttled them back. What a weapon an admission of love would give him against her. In his present black mood, he wouldn't hesitate to use it and she couldn't bear to have her feelings thrown in her face. If he even chose to believe her. 'Katie was the reason we married,' she reminded him in a subdued voice.

'Of course.' His gaze burned into her, into her very soul. The shock of her revelation was finally getting through to him, she assumed. And he was reacting precisely as she had feared he would.

What had she expected? Reassurance that everything would be all right? A promise to stand by her no matter what the future held? Only true love could create such a bond. Being good together in bed wasn't nearly enough.

'Isn't there some sort of genetic test which can be done to establish whether or not you carry the gene?' he asked.

Wearily, she shook her head. 'You need grandparents and parents who can be tested to establish a genetic pattern. I don't have enough living relatives for a test to be conclusive.'

His bleak expression told her nothing. 'Do you have any more surprises in store for me, Eden?'

Bitterness surged through her. 'Isn't today's news enough for anyone?'

He moved towards her but she shrank back. 'It's all right, I don't need your pity.'

He froze in mid-step. 'Pity wasn't what I had in mind, but you probably wouldn't know the difference.'

He thrust past her and the door slammed, separating them. She stayed where she was for a long time, her heart aching as she heard him drive away. Finally she went upstairs and lay down, letting sleep replace the tears she was afraid to cry in case she couldn't stop.

Hours later, she awoke heavy-eyed and disorientated. Ellen and Katie were playing a board game downstairs but Slade was still missing. 'Did Slade say what time he'd be back?' she asked the housekeeper, although she was terrified she already knew the answer.

'I haven't heard from him since Katie and I got back after lunch. Is there anything I can do, dear? You're as white as a ghost.'

There was nothing anyone could do. Slade had turned his back on her. Was it any wonder that she hadn't volunteered her secret?

Somehow she got through the day and the one that followed without alarming Katie. With no word from Slade, it was a supreme effort to act as if nothing was wrong when her world had crumbled around her. She visited her mother and pottered around the house and garden, wondering what she would do if he never came back into her life.

It took a telephone call from his secretary to jolt her back to life. 'I'm at my wits' end,' she said. 'Mr Benedict hasn't called in and I need answers on several of his projects.'

Eden knew the girl well from her own days at Benedict Communications. She asked for a summary of the projects which were on hold during Slade's absence. As the secretary talked, an idea began to form in her mind. 'I'm familiar with most of those projects so I should be able to help,' she said. 'I'll be in as soon as I can.'

She could sense the other woman's scepticism and smiled. The expression felt strange, as if her facial muscles had atrophied. She hadn't done much smiling lately. But the idea of going to Slade's office challenged her. As his wife she was co-owner of the company, and she knew as much about its workings as anyone there. She might not be much of a wife, but she could prove herself in other ways.

It was immensely satisfying to sail into the building and go straight to the executive offices, bypassing her old cubbyhole in the research department. The buzz of talk followed her but she kept her face impassive. This time she would give them something else to gossip about besides her love life.

Slade's secretary had the files open on his desk when Eden arrived. She assessed them steadily and made some quick decisions, surprising herself with how quickly she grasped what needed to be done.

Her former co-worker from Research, Denise, appeared in answer to her summons. 'Production tells me they're held up until you provide background for the last educational video,' Eden said, her tone intentionally brisk.

Denise's mouth dropped open. 'I have almost all the material, Eden . . . Mrs Benedict.'

'Almost won't do it. They need the stuff by five this afternoon. Pull someone out of Secretarial if you need an extra pair of hands.'

'Yes, Mrs Benedict.' There was a new respect in Denise's tone as she picked up the files and left. Now we're even for lunch, Eden thought although she chided herself for being petty. Nobody's perfect, she consoled herself.

She had been right to come here. Clearing Slade's desk gave her little time for thinking about her own concerns. But subconsciously the decision-making process had continued. By the end of the afternoon her mind was made up. If Slade would agree, she would remain as his wife until Katie came of age. He hadn't wanted a love match in the first place, so the proposal should suit him. Then she would take her family problems and disappear from his life. Cutting out her heart would be easier, she acknowledged, but what else could she do?

Tears began to film her eyes and she forced herself to concentrate on the file in front of her. It was already late. The office had emptied around her an hour ago. But the thought of going home to a house without Slade kept her at the desk.

Suddenly her shriek tore the air as a dark figure loomed over her. It was Slade and her heart turned over, until she got herself under control, at least outwardly. 'You gave me a fright. What are you doing here?'

His expression was impassive. 'I understood it was my office.'

She half rose, but he motioned her to remain seated. It was just as well. Her legs felt boneless and her heartbeat was so erratic that she wondered if she was going to faint for the first time in her life. It was as if she had conjured him up out of her deep longings.

He looked as if the last couple of days had taken a toll. A bluish shadow darkened his jawline, and his eyes seemed deeper-set, the hollows of his cheekbones more pronounced. Rather than face his censure, she concentrated on his hands, which gripped the edge of the desk. The sight reminded her so forcibly of his touch, exploring every inch of her body with intimate assurance, that she closed her eyes. If she was to retain any vestige of dignity, she couldn't afford to look at him at all.

'I decided to make myself useful,' she explained, fixing her gaze at a point beyond his shoulder.

'Of course. I'd expect nothing less.'

His tone mocked her and her anger rose. 'If you object to my being here, please say so.'

'I object to your being here.'

Fighting back tears, she closed the files and gathered her personal papers, then started for the door.

Her way was blocked by his body and she froze. 'I'd rather you were at home, looking after Katie and planning how many brothers and sisters she should have.'

Why was he being so cruel? 'That isn't fair or funny, Slade.'

He lifted the files from her arms and dropped them on to a side-table. 'I know. You aren't the only one who's been making themselves useful over the last few days.'

Another wave of faintness swept through her. 'What do you mean?'

'I've been tracing your family tree.'

'What's the point? If you hoped to find enough relatives for the genetic test, you've been on a wild-goose chase. Neither of us gets off that easily.'

'I didn't want any easy option. I wanted the truth.'

'Which sometimes hurts,' she admitted softly.

'And sometimes it helps.' He steered her to a leather couch. 'Sit down, Eden. What I discovered may come as a shock to you.'

It couldn't be a greater shock than the feel of his hands against her bare arms. It was a lover's touch, warm and gentle, and it was a poignant reminder of all she could have had.

He steered her to a chair and urged her to sit down. Then he took her hands. 'There's no easy way to tell you this, but Peggy Lyle isn't your real mother.'

She shook her head, unwilling to accept what she was hearing. 'No, I don't believe it.'

His grip tightened around her fingers. 'You must believe it, darling. I found out when I went hunting for your relatives to help you with the genetic testing.'

As she saw what he was getting at, fury blazed through her mind and she tore her hands free. 'You wanted to find out if I was worth keeping as a wife, is that it?'

'Good lord, no. Nothing was further from my mind.' He dropped to his knees beside her and took her unyielding body in his arms. 'I know this is a shock to you. You aren't thinking too clearly right now, and no wonder. The only reason I went looking for your relatives was for your sake, to save you years of waiting and wondering. I did it for you, Eden, because I care about you. Your happiness and peace of mind mean more to me than anything else.'

She pressed her face into her hands. Slade had gone searching for her relatives and found that she had no one, not even her mother. 'This must be what Peggy tried to steel herself to tell me,' she whispered. If only she had, how much closer they could have been all these years.

'By the time she was really ill, she was probably afraid to take the risk. She needed you too much.' His expression hardened. 'Although she could have spared you so much torment if she'd told you when she was first diagnosed.'

Eden nodded numbly. 'Even her doctor can't have known I was adopted or he'd have reassured me when he explained what was wrong with her.' Suddenly she turned wide, anxious eyes to him. 'So who am I? Who are my real parents?'

He stroked the hair back from her forehead. 'Don't fret about it now, darling. We'll find out everything you need to know. I'll use every resource at my disposal, I promise.'

Her eyes swam as she nodded her thanks. 'I don't know what to say. All these years, I never suspected . . .'

As her voice broke on a sob, his arms tightened around her. 'I know how hard this must be to accept, but think what else it means to you.'

She didn't want to think, didn't want to face any more shocks. She felt rootless, cut adrift from all she had known and loved all her life. None of it belonged to her. She was a changeling.

The only reality was Slade's rock-steady hold on her. Had she really heard him say he cared and call her his darling? Could it be that he really did feel something for her, after all?

Her breath tangled in her throat as she fought the hope welling insistently inside her. But she was forced to accept the facts. He hadn't deserted her, as she'd feared. He'd gone searching for her family for *her* sake, not because he needed reassurance, but because he knew *she* did.

'Oh, my lord,' she breathed as realisation finally came. 'If I'm adopted, then I don't have...I'm not...'

He pressed her hands to his lips. 'I'd rather think of what you *do* have—a healthy future filled with promise.'

'I feel reborn,' she confessed, her voice rising. 'You've given me the greatest gift in the world.'

Unthinkingly, she flung her arms around his neck. His own tightened around her and he cradled her against his chest. 'I've given you no more than you deserve—a lifetime of happiness,' he said thickly. 'I hope you'll use it to the fullest, to have the marriage and children of your dreams.'

Fresh anguish gripped her as his words penetrated the mists of happiness fogging her mind.

'What do you mean? I thought I already had those things in you and Katie.'

He took a long, shuddering breath. 'You're sure? Our marriage is what you really want?'

'More than anything in the world.'

His laughter erupted between them. 'Hallelujah! You don't know how much it means to me to hear you say so. I thought once you found out there was no reason you couldn't marry for love . . .'

Her finger pressed against his lips, silencing him. 'I already married for love. But I thought you were the one who didn't want a hearts-and-flowers marriage.'

'Some men don't know what's good for them,' he said, his eyes glowing as he looked at her. 'Thank goodness I had you to show me what I was missing.'

'Even though I bluffed my way into working for you?' she asked, unable to resist the teasing reminder.

'Even then. I told myself I was a fool but it didn't seem to help. Now I know why you had to do it— to get the job and promotion you needed to care for your mother—so my instincts about you were right all along.'

Her breath caught in her throat. 'But you became so distant. I thought you'd lost interest in me.'

'My God, it was the opposite. I wanted you so much I was afraid I'd scare you away. It almost killed me to leave you alone but I was determined to give you breathing space. I hope you'd discover you loved me after all.'

'I do love you,' she confessed in a rush. 'But I thought you didn't want it because of your father.'

He nodded. 'Given my family's track record, was it any wonder that I was cynical about love? Until I found myself falling in love with you in spite of everything. I knew it was a lost cause when I found myself wanting to tear apart the men I thought you were seeing.'

The strength of his passion made her heart swell. 'There was never anyone but you,' she confided.

'I know it now. I understand about the pills and the mysterious absences. But love isn't logical. I thought you'd guessed how I felt when I told Dana why I'd married you.'

'I thought you said it for her sake. I never dreamed that you really meant it.'

'Maybe this will convince you.' He swept her into his arms and sought her mouth, his kiss more gentle yet more passionate than she could have dreamed possible. When her mouth opened, he invaded the moist cavern with mind-shattering thoroughness, leaving her in no doubt that she was well and truly loved.

Suddenly she remembered where they were. 'What if someone comes in?' she asked.

The hunger in his eyes intensified as he began to undo the buttons of her businesslike blouse. 'They won't,' he said thickly. 'The building is locked and I've instructed Security not to admit anyone.'

They were finally alone together and her heart began to pound. 'What *do* you have in mind?' she teased, knowing full well.

With loving efficiency, he proceeded to show her. She would never be able to look at this couch again without picturing this night and blushing, she realised. It was just as well she wouldn't be spending much time in the office in future.

In the dreamy aftermath, she regarded him curiously. 'What happened to change your mind about love and marriage?'

He stroked her hair. 'You happened, my darling. You're enough to change any man's mind. No matter what my searches uncovered, I still intended to come back to you. I promised you "for better or worse" and I meant it, my love.'

Her heart sang. She had both her love and her future. It was almost more than she could take in. 'I love you, too,' she said, her voice shaking with emotion. 'You've given me so much. My life, in fact. How can I ever repay you?'

His arms tightening around her left no room for doubt. 'How about one kiss at a time?' he suggested huskily.

Her delighted laughter greeted this idea. 'At that rate, it could take a while.'

He kissed her again, his body hardening deliciously against her. 'A lifetime, I imagine. And it won't be nearly long enough.'

As he pulled her down on to the couch, her sigh of ecstasy signalled complete agreement. A lifetime of Slade's love. What more could she possibly want?

4 FREE

Romances and 2 FREE gifts just for you!

*You can enjoy all the
heartwarming emotion of true love for FREE!
Discover the heartbreak and happiness,
the emotion and the tenderness of the modern
relationships in Mills & Boon Romances.*

*We'll send you 4 Romances as a special offer
from Mills & Boon Reader Service,
along with the opportunity to have 6 captivating
new Romances delivered to your door each month.*

Claim your FREE books and gifts overleaf...

An irresistible offer from Mills & Boon

Become a regular reader of Romances with Mills & Boon Reader Service and we'll welcome you with 4 books, a CUDDLY TEDDY and a special MYSTERY GIFT all absolutely FREE.

And then look forward to receiving 6 brand new Romances each month, delivered to your door hot off the presses, postage and packing FREE! Plus our free Newsletter featuring author news, competitions, special offers and much more.

This invitation comes with no strings attached. You may cancel or suspend your subscription at any time, and still keep your free books and gifts.

It's so easy. Send no money now. Simply fill in the coupon below and post it to -
Reader Service, FREEPOST, PO Box 236, Croydon, Surrey CR9 9EL.

NO STAMP REQUIRED

Free Books Coupon

Yes! Please rush me 4 FREE Romances and 2 FREE gifts! Please also reserve me a Reader Service subscription. If I decide to subscribe I can look forward to receiving 6 brand new Romances for just £10.80 each month, postage and packing FREE. If I decide not to subscribe I shall write to you within 10 days - I can keep the free books and gifts whatever I choose. I may cancel or suspend my subscription at any time. I am over 18 years of age.

Ms/Mrs/Miss/Mr _____ EP56R

Address _____

_____

Postcode _____ Signature _____

Offers closes 31st March 1994. The right is reserved to refuse an application and change the terms of this offer. This offer does not apply to Romance subscribers. One application per household. Overseas readers please write for details. Southern Africa write to Book Services International Ltd., Box 41654, Craighall, Transvaal 2024. You may be mailed with offers from other reputable companies as a result of this application. Please tick box if you would prefer not to receive such offers. ☐

mps MAILING PREFERENCE SERVICE

Next Month's Romances

Each month you can choose from a wide variety of romance with Mills & Boon. Below are the new titles to look out for next month, why not ask either Mills & Boon Reader Service or your Newsagent to reserve you a copy of the titles you want to buy – just tick the titles you would like and either post to Reader Service or take it to any Newsagent and ask them to order your books.

Please save me the following titles:	Please tick	√
UNWILLING MISTRESS	Lindsay Armstrong	
DARK HERITAGE	Emma Darcy	
WOUNDS OF PASSION	Charlotte Lamb	
LOST IN LOVE	Michelle Reid	
ORIGINAL SIN	Rosalie Ash	
SUDDEN FIRE	Elizabeth Oldfield	
THE BRIDE OF SANTA BARBARA	Angela Devine	
ISLAND OF SHELLS	Grace Green	
LOVE'S REVENGE	Mary Lyons	
MAKING MAGIC	Karen van der Zee	
OASIS OF THE HEART	Jessica Hart	
BUILD A DREAM	Quinn Wilder	
A BRIDE TO LOVE	Barbara McMahon	
A MAN CALLED TRAVERS	Brittany Young	
A CHILD CALLED MATTHEW	Sara Grant	
DANCE OF SEDUCTION	Vanessa Grant	

If you would like to order these books in addition to your regular subscription from Mills & Boon Reader Service please send £1.80 per title to: Mills & Boon Reader Service, Freepost, P.O. Box 236, Croydon, Surrey, CR9 9EL, quote your Subscriber No:................................... (If applicable) and complete the name and address details below. Alternatively, these books are available from many local Newsagents including W.H.Smith, J.Menzies, Martins and other paperback stockists from 14 January 1994.

Name:...

Address:..

.....................................Post Code:.............................

To Retailer: If you would like to stock M&B books please contact your regular book/magazine wholesaler for details.

You may be mailed with offers from other reputable companies as a result of this application.
If you would rather not take advantage of these opportunities please tick box ☐